art day

M781.620969 Kelly.J
Folk songs Hawaii sings /
compiled, arranged & annotated
by John M. Kelly.

M784.4
K 297f
cop.1

OCT 28 '80

NOV 23 1979

EVANSTON PUBLIC LIBRARY
EVANSTON, ILLINOIS

Five cents a day is charged for adult books kept over time; two cents a day for children.

The borrower is responsible for books charged to his name and for mutilation unless reported at time of issue.

M781.620969
Kelly.J

FOLK SONGS HAWAII SINGS

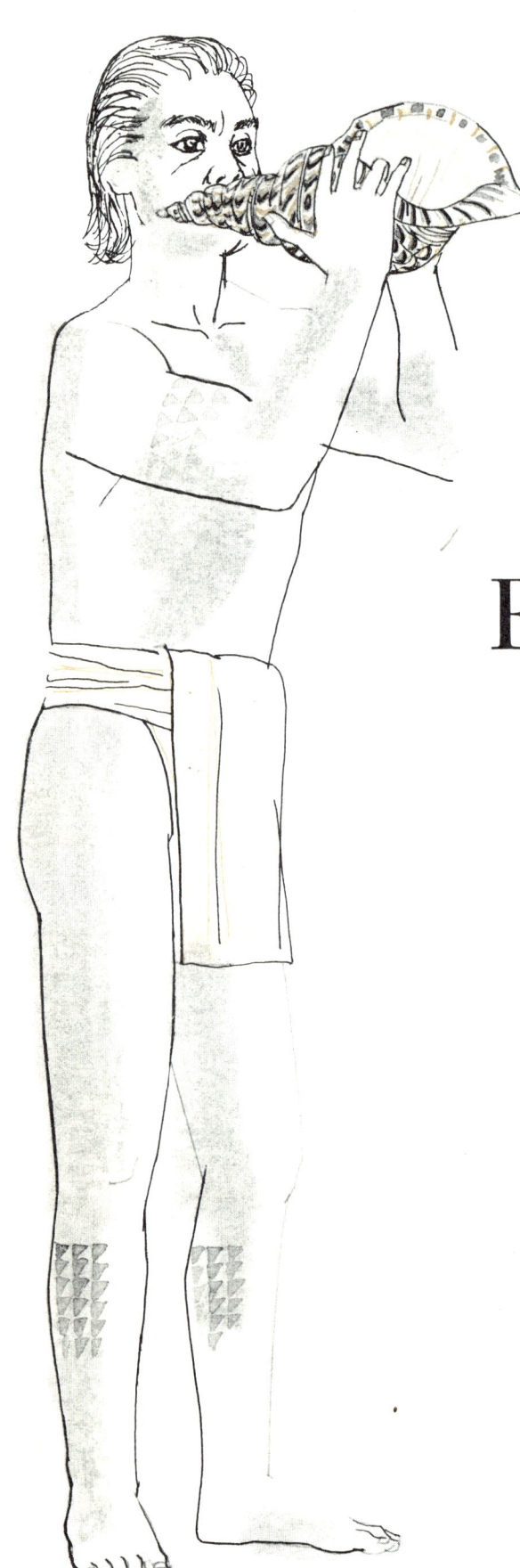

FOLK SONGS

HAWAII SINGS

Compiled, arranged & annotated by

JOHN M. KELLY, Jr.

Illustrated by

KEICHI KIMURA

CHARLES E. TUTTLE COMPANY, INC.
Rutland, Vermont & Tokyo, Japan

This book was written with the financial assistance of the McInerny Foundation, Honolulu, and is published by arrangement with the Palama Settlement, Honolulu.

European Representatives
Continent: BOXERBOOKS, INC., Zurich
British Isles: PRENTICE-HALL INTERNATIONAL, INC., London

Published by the
Charles E. Tuttle Company, Inc.
of Rutland, Vermont & Tokyo, Japan
with editorial offices at
15 Edogawa-cho, Bunkyo-ku, Tokyo

Copyright in Japan, 1962
by Charles E. Tuttle Company, Inc.
All rights reserved

Library of Congress Catalog
Card No. 62-14118

First edition, 1963

Book design & typography
by M. Weatherby & Ken Tremayne
Printed in Japan

Table of Contents

Foreword	7
MUSIC OF POLYNESIA	11
HAWAII	
Farewell to Thee: *Aloha 'Oe*	14
The Garland Flowers of Hawaii: *Na Lei o Hawaii*	17
My Sweetheart Surfing: *Ku'u Ipo I Ka He'e Pu'eone*	20
The Opening Flower: *Makalapua*	23
Sassy: *Sasy*	26
Famed Are the Roughriders: *Kilakila na Roughrider*	28
The Thirsty Winds of Kohala: *Ka Inuwai*	30
I Went to Hilo	32
SAMOA	
Come, Dance: *Siva Siva Maia*	34
UVEA	
The Bonito Leap: *Atu Langoto*	36

5

MUSIC OF ASIA — 39

JAPAN

Cherry Blossoms: *Sakura*	42
Honorable Koto: *On-koto*	44
Song of Kiso: *Kiso Bushi*	46
It's Open: *Hiraita*	48
Sound of Running Feet: *Kutsu ga Naru*	50
Song of Menuhama: *Menuhama Bushi*	52

PHILIPPINES

Leron, Leron, My Dear: *Leron, Leron, Sinta*	54
Planting Rice: *Magtanim Ay Di Biro*	56
My Nipa Hut: *Bahai Kubo*	58

CHINA

Mongolian Love Song: *Meng-ku Ching Ko*	60
New Moon Over Kangting: *Kang-ting Shing Yueh*	63
Blue Flower: *Lan Hua-hua*	66

KOREA

Song of Bluebells: *Doraji Tahryung*	69
Hills of Arirang: *Arirang*	72
A New Spring is Coming: *Keh-gi-na-ching-ching-nah-neh*	74
Song of Roasted Chestnuts: *Kunbam Tahryung*	76
Weaving Song: *Tuhl Tahryung*	78

Pronunciation Guide	80
Selected Bibliography	80

Hawaiian playing a nose flute

Foreword

The folk music of Hawaii is a living blend of the cultures of people from all over the world, particularly from lands washed by the Pacific Ocean. In addition to informal singing, there are the devoted efforts of both practiced and unpracticed performing groups that keep alive the music of Japan, Okinawa, Korea, China, the Philippines, Micronesia, and Polynesia.

A number of institutions in Hawaii are increasingly active in the promotion and preservation of the authentic folk music of the Pacific peoples including the University of Hawaii, Bishop Museum, Kamehameha Schools, Laie Church College, and others. Japanese Bon Festival music and dancing attract many thousands of participants during the summer months. Several Ryukyuan groups can at any time assemble one or two score of skilled players of the *koto* (Japanese harp) for song and dance programs. Nearly every man, woman, and child of Samoan descent can perform countless dances and songs filled with the vigorous clapping and body-slapping movements of their tradition. Filipino *fiestas*, evenings of music and dances of Micronesia performed by Micronesian students, Hawaiian hula and song contests, and innumerable pageants, Chinese Narcissus Festivals, and the like keep Hawaii musically active throughout the year.

Some of these traditions have had to survive great pressures. At the start of World War II many Japanese burned their drums, instruments, and other symbols of their heritage. During the nineteenth century, missionary influences were brought to bear against ancient Hawaiian chants and dances. And the desire to conform to American standards on the part of many incoming peoples, especially among the second-generation youth, tends to weaken their old-country traditions.

Then, of course, folk songs of agrarian origin do not flourish in a modern commercial-industrial community. A rice-harvest song may seem only quaint to the modern generation when one need only slip behind the wheel, drive five minutes to the super-market and buy a bag of polished, vitamin-enriched rice for the equivalent of scarcely half an hour's work. Times have changed. Finishing the arduous work of planting and harvesting the crops by hand is what made these songs such a joy to sing in the old days.

Topping all challenges to folk music is that of commercial radio and television, which has made the present generation an audience of non-participating onlookers. Such a condition is the mortal enemy of the "folk process."

Despite all these obstacles, folk music still lives among all nationality groups in Hawaii, offering resources for performance, education, and entertainment. Unfortunately, only a very small number of the songs, to say nothing of the dances, have been collected, notated, and made available in English—a fact which provides sufficient excuse for the modest collection offered here.

Folklorists hesitate to define a folk song other than to say that to be genuine it must have been orally transmitted, have variant versions, and be anonymous or at least have several claims to authorship. A few songs in this book, such as "Farewell to Thee" and "Sound of Running Feet," do not strictly fulfill all these requirements. They have been included, however, as cousins to those that do and because they are notably representative of important styles of song literature that enjoy the status of folk song.

With apologies to purists among folk singers, justification is offered for this set of piano arrangements, all by the present writer, of folk songs originating in cultures where not only was the piano foreign but also all it represents historically in the way of harmony, counterpoint, and sonority. It is simply that the songs become accessible through a familiar medium. It is hoped that further steps will be taken to hear the songs in their native settings through LP recordings now available.

In Western music the piano is often used to represent a voice, drum, orchestra, or chorus—and just about every other musical instrument as well—with varying degrees of effectiveness. In making the piano arrangements given here, the intention was to give songs that belong to other instruments as friendly a setting as possible for the piano, while at the same time preserving as much as possible the qualities and elements of the native settings. It is hoped the reader will understand the serious limitations involved.

Harmony is an element of Western music not germane to the old music of Asia. Except where the songs may have been created under Western influences, the attempt has been made here to avoid diatonic chordal accompaniments. Instead, the parts for left hand, added to give sonority and depth, have generally been developed as implied by the melodic structure. In no case has a single note of the original melody been altered for the sake of the accompaniment. If a version seems different from a more familiar one, it is probably due to normal differences existing regionally and chronologically as in all folk-song literature.

To make the collection appealing to both those with and those without piano technique, accompaniments of varying degrees of difficulty have been included.

Western notation is not truly adequate for writing Asian melodies. Many in-between tones are heard in performance that cannot be indicated. These inflections and embellishments vary with the performer, as in all folk music, and are a basic feature of Asian music. It is as though the melody as we would notate it were a skeleton around which all performers build the real personality of the song. Notwithstanding this problem, much strength and beauty is found even in the basic outlines of the melodies, which are all that can be given in such a collection as this.

Probably the most popular single type of instrument for the accompanying of folk songs throughout Asia and the Pacific islands is the drum or some equivalent rhythm instrument such as the bamboo slit-gong. There are many different kinds of drums, gourds, and other percussion instruments, including huge Japanese ceremonial drums mounted on special carts, Hawaii's small coconut-shell drums used by dancers, and even pebbles held in the hand. Also widely used are various forms of flutes and stringed instruments.

With regard to the English translations of the song lyrics presented here, again difficulties arise from the great differences in language structures. Sometimes it has been possible to give nothing more than an unsingable paraphrase. But wherever it has been possible without serious affront to original poetry and melody, singable verses in English have been given. Unless stated otherwise, all the English versions have been adapted by the present writer from translations kindly provided by the persons indicated.

Although the conditions of living that generated most of the folk culture of Hawaii and the Pacific nations have radically altered and in many ways disappeared altogether, it is a matter of great interest to preserve and popularize these symbols of a former way of life. Not only are there beautiful natural works of art among folk songs but they have such a way of preserving the hopes and aspirations, the struggles for a better life, the joys and hardships of the old days, and of today as well, that it behooves us to understand them better.

The Portuguese, Puerto Ricans, and others peoples of European origin have also contributed much to the folk culture of Hawaii. However, their songs of Western origin, are already available in existing publications. It was considered desirable to devote this volume to songs of Polynesian and Asian origin, which are less known and practically unavailable in print.

Much appreciation is due the many folk musicians and others who generously contributed their knowledge and experience to this project. Among these, special thanks are extended to Mary Kawena Pukui, a leading authority in Hawaiiana; Patria Abella, teacher of native songs and music of the Philippines; Halla Huhm, dancer, drummer, and singer of both the folk and classical music of Korea; Keum Nyu Park, music teacher, linguist in Korean, Japanese, and English; Dr. Charles Tien Wei Yun, who, with extensive knowledge and encouragement, helped with the Chinese folk songs.

The Administration, Board of Trustees, and Music Advisory Committee of Palama Settlement, a Honolulu Community Chest Agency, have supported this research and publishing project since its inception, as has also the McInerny Foundation of Honolulu, with two generous grants. Their help is gratefully acknowledged.

Most of the songs and arrangements given here have made up the experimental and concert repertory of the Palama Settlement Children's Chorus in recent years. To the members of that chorus the author expresses fondest *aloha* and thanks for their many hours of devoted singing.

Honolulu, 1962

JOHN M. KELLY, JR.

MUSIC OF POLYNESIA

THE MUSIC OF MOST OF THE PACIFIC ISLANDS divides itself generally between that which existed among native peoples before contact with Europeans and that which has developed in post-European times.

Very little pre-European music and dance exists today. That which has been preserved has, in many cases, lost its functional meaning. During the period of European exploration, trade, commercial exploitation, and Christianization in the Pacific in the eighteenth and nineteenth centuries, many native customs were supplanted with Western mores. Some were suppressed by laws and edicts.

The peoples of Polynesia had developed no written languages prior to contact with the West. Knowledge and productive skills, social sanctions, geneologies, personal and community experiences, and the imagery arising from man's relation to nature were embodied in music and dance. Together with the spoken language, music and dance were the main vehicles of communication. They served in many ways as libraries and schools. The teaching of these arts as vital parts of community life was often invested with the most sacred and powerful sanctions.

Most of the music of Polynesia sung and played today is made up of forms and characteristics lingering on from ancient times combined with elements borrowed from Western music. The ancient vocal music throughout the Pacific islands was confined to chants using one, two, three, or at the most, four tones. What the melodies lacked in tonal freedom was compensated for by the use of subtle inflection in the handling of words. Rhythm predominated in the old music, being used extensively not only with dancing but also with such vital community activities as digging, planting, hauling nets and logs, war training, ground stamping for planting, and similar ceremonies.

After contact with the first Europeans, the songs extended their scope, eventually employing all the melodic resources of the seven-tone diatonic scales and the techniques of part singing in harmony. Foreign words and phrases entered the songs, while the subject matter shifted from the imagery and experiences of the old communal order to the more individualized sentiments of the new.

Some of the old formal characteristics are retained in today's music, such as rhythmic patterns and the language, but an entirely new content has been poured into the old molds. It is this new content, the changed relations among people and between the social order and nature that has

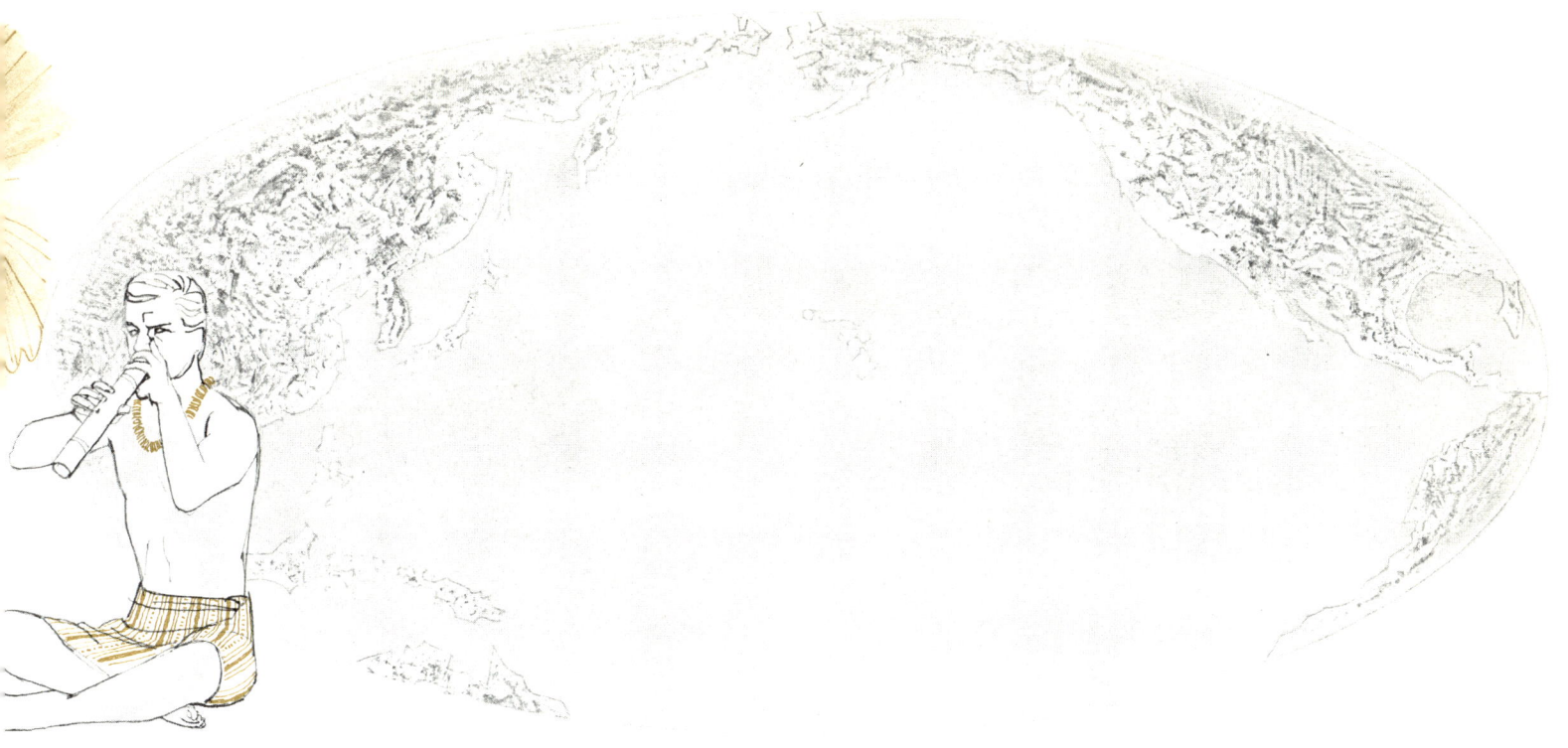

completely altered the music, dance, and the entire culture of the peoples of the Pacific islands.

In Hawaii, what may be considered Hawaiian folk music today are the anonymous songs popular since the late nineteenth century that were passed around orally among the people and performed with ukulele and guitar accompaniment. They are generally known as hula songs, several examples being included here. These hula songs are short, quick-tempo songs used for general entertainment and informal dancing. They are participation songs: everyone joins in the fun and sings the same couplet verses after the soloist, and even *tutu* (grandma) gets up and does a few hula steps with a dignity befitting her age. The form of these songs is a union of pre-European native dance-and-chant forms with the freer melody and the diatonic harmony brought in from the West. They are sometimes called *hapa haole* (half-white) songs.

Within a few years after the arrival in Hawaii of the first hymn-singing missionaries in 1820, the native Hawaiians were singing their new religion in four-part harmony, and the style of song which developed from this singing came to be known as *himeni,* after the word hymn. By the late 1800's the subject matter of the *himeni* had reverted to the secular, as may be seen in such examples as "Farewell to Thee," "The Opening Flower," "The Thirsty Winds of Kohala," and "My Sweetheart Surfing." In a strict sense, the *himeni* were sung unaccompanied, with solo verses and four-part choruses, and generally a slow and dignified tempo. They were never accompanied by dancing, which for a period in missionary Hawaii was actually prohibited. The same style of singing developed in other areas of the Pacific, where it is referred to as *himine* rather than *himeni*.

In the *himeni* songs of Hawaii the subject is often an expression of intense longing for some place or person that is far away. This may reflect the extensive movements of population that took place after European contact. One of Kamehameha's ways of "uniting" the Hawaiian Islands under his crown was to disperse people from one area to another to destroy the political and social unity of his opposition. In addition, in the nineteenth century many Hawaiians left the islands on whalers and trading ships and traveled throughout the seven seas. Thus many of the *himeni* are imbued with a longing for the beautiful valleys of the homeland or yearning for someone who has gone away. Most *himeni* were verses set to borrowed tunes, such as "Farewell to Thee," by well-known verse writers, including Hawaiian royalty.

ALOHA ʻOE
Farewell to Thee
HAWAII

"ALOHA ʻOE" is Hawaii's most famous song. Although far from being anonymous—Queen Liliuokalani, Hawaii's prolific song-writing monarch, composed the verses in 1878, a few years before the turbulent end of the Hawaiian kingdom—it occupies a place in the hearts of the people of Hawaii comparable to that of the best-known folk songs.

The tune of the verse is remarkably close to "The Rock Beside the Sea," by the American composer Charles Crozat Converse, published in Philadelphia in 1857, while the chorus tune is attributed by Sigmund Spaeth to the chorus of George Frederick Root's "There's Music in the Air," published in 1854.

Mary Kawena Pukui remembers the story told by Lahilahi Webb—both ladies being among Hawaii's most outstanding historians— of a visit by the queen and her attendants to Maunawili, a lovely mountain retreat on the windward side of Oahu just below the famous *pali* (cliff). As the party mounted their horses for the return to Honolulu, the queen's imagination was caught by the affectionate parting of a young man in her company and a lovely girl of the locality. As the party rode home the queen was humming softly, and the verses of "Aloha ʻOe" came into being.

There exists in the George R. Carter Memorial Collection of the Bishop Museum a manuscript copy of both words and music for "Aloha ʻOe" in the hand of Queen Liliuokalani herself. A careful comparison of this with the song as usually sung today provides an interesting example of the "folk process" at work, a process by means of which even this most-loved song of Hawaii was gradually altered by time and usage until it became more perfect than the original version. There are now at least nine published versions of the song, each one differing only in details.

The version given here is perhaps as close to the original manner of singing as it is possible to get while still preserving the improvements spoken of above. This has been made possible through the assistance of several "old-timers," particularly Lena Machado, famous "Songbird of Hawaii," over whose singing of "Aloha ʻOe" many thousands have wept tears of joy and sadness on "boat day" and at the concerts of the Royal Hawaiian Band at Kapiolani Park. Kamokila Campbell, Mary Kawena Pukui, and others remember Queen Liliuokalani's original way of singing the words *Aloha ʻoe* which open the chorus, and they are given here in that same manner.

The piano accompaniment avoids the pounding swing-bass style which tends to obscure the tender sentiments of this lovely song. However, no single accompaniment can at the same time serve both the intimacy of one's own home and the larger dimensions of a mass-singing performance. For the latter it may be necessary for the pianist to augment the piano part with octaves or use another style altogether.

"Aloha ʻOe" is in the tradition of the *himeni* singing (see page 13). It should be sung and accompanied with care as to phrasing and sentiment. The chorus may be sung in four parts or as a duet using soprano and alto parts. The English lyrics differ only slightly from Queen Liliuokalani's original English.

GLOSSARY: *Liko,* a tender leaf bud. *ʻAhihi lehua,* a low spreading bush (Metrosiderous) formerly plentiful in Nuuanu Valley, where it still may be found, shrub-like with twisted trunk, clinging to the windward slopes.

QUEEN LILIUOKALANI: NEW ENGLISH ADAPTATION BY J.K.   QUEEN LILIUOKALANI

14 Folk Songs Hawaii Sings

Ha-'a - he-o e kau-a i na pa - li, Ke ni-hi a-'e a la i ka na - he - le, E u-
Proud-ly sweeps the rain o'er the pa - li, And soft - ly glides a-mong the trees,___ Ev-er

hai a-na pa-ha i ka li - ko, Pu-a 'a - hi-hi le-hu-a a o u - ka.
fol - low-ing the bud-ding li - ko, The 'a - hi-hi le-hu-a of the up - lands.

* Chording for guitar or ukulele accompaniment is in easier key of A major.

** Variant

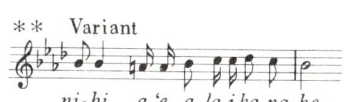

ni-hi a-'e a la i ka na-he-

Music of Polynesia 15

2 *O ka halia 'loha i hiki mai,*
   Ke hone ae nei i ku 'u manawa,
   O 'oe no kau ipo aloha,
   A loko e hana nei.

   CHORUS

3 *Maopopo ku'u i ka nani,*
   Na pua rose o Maunawili;
   Ilaila hiaui na manu,
   Aloko e hana nei.

   CHORUS

When sweet memories come back to me,
Bringing fresh remembrance of the past—
Dearest one, yes, thou art mine own;
From thee true love shall ne'er depart.

CHORUS

I have seen and watched thy loveliness,
Thou sweet rose of Maunawili;
And 'tis there the birds oft love to dwell,
And sip the honey from thy lips.

CHORUS

NA LEI O HAWAII
The Garland Flowers of Hawaii
HAWAII

This song, also known as "The Eight Islands" *(Na Moku Ewalu),* was composed by the Reverend Samuel Kapu in the 1890's, being the earliest of several songs with the same title. A pageant was organized at that time, the first of its kind, in which a succession of dancers presented leis representing each of the eight main islands. Tiny, uninhabited Molokini, though without flower or other symbol, was also included in the song. Both the song and the pageant celebrated the uniting of the islands into the Kingdom of Hawaii. The concept of all the islands belonging to one domain had not existed in times before the monarchy.

The English lyrics adhere as closely as possible to the meaning of the original Hawaiian words. Syllables marked with two accent marks are to be sung in two or more notes. The song is in the informal hula style (see page 13).

Included is a list of the flower symbols of the main islands. The flowers, stems, berries, leaves, and shells listed are usually strung into leis as decorative symbols of their respective islands. Leis are made by stringing such materials on a length of thread and then tying the ends of the thread together to make a garland necklace. These are given as tokens of love and affection, and it is said the circular shape may represent a mother's arms encircling her baby.

GLOSSARY: Verse 1: *Keawe,* a great chief of ancient times on the island of Hawaii; under his leadership the people of the island attained a bountiful life, and an unidentified southern star was later named in his honor.

Verse 2: *Haleakala,* literally "house of the sun," an extinct volcano and the world's tallest mountain reckoning from the ocean floor.

Verse 3: *Hina,* the goddess-mother of Molokai. *Lanikaula,* a great native prophet of ancient times.

Verse 8: *Laua'e o Makana,* a sweet fern of Makana, Kauai.

Verses 10 and 11: *Ha'ina ia mai ana kapuana,* the concluding phrase to most Hawaiian hula songs, derived from the ancient Hawaiian chant meaning literally, "Tell the summary refrain." *Hiiaka,* the youngest and favorite sister of *Pele,* mythical Polynesian goddess of fire and of the volcanoes, to whose originating creative power tribute is usually made at the conclusion of songs, chants, and narratives; Hiiaka is said to have traveled extensively in the seas between the islands.

Music of Polynesia 17

18 *Folk Songs Hawaii Sings*

2 *Kilakila o Maui Haleakala,*
  Ua kapu Roselani nau hoʻokahi.
3 *Kaulana Molokai nui a Hina,*
  I ka ulu kukui o Lanikaula.
4 *Lei ana Lanai i ke kaunaʻoa*
  Me he manu ʻoʻo hulu melemele.
5 *Eia mai au Kahoolawe,*
  Hoʻoheno ana au me ka hinahina.
6 *Hea aku makou o mai ʻoe;*
  Molokini ʻalo ke ʻehu o ke kai.
7 *Kaulana Oahu i ka ʻilima,*
  Kohu kapa ʻahuʻula kau poʻohiwi.
8 *Kaulana Kauai i ka mokihana,*
  Lauaʻe o Makana kau aloha.
9 *Pupu Niihau auheaʻoe,*
  Hoike aʻe ʻoe a i ko nani.
10 *Haʻina ia mai ana kapuana,*
  Na lei o Hawaii e o mai.
11 *Haʻina hou ia mai ana ka puana,*
  Hiʻiaka ia ka poli a o Pele.

Surmounting regal Maui, Haleakala,
  Reserv'd is *roselani* for you alone.
Renounéd Molokai, great isle of Hina,
  The *kukui* grove of Lanikaula.
The lei of Lanai, sweet *kaunaʻoa,*
  Like the *ʻoʻo* bird's lovely yellow feathers.
Here I am waiting, Kahoolawe,
  Abounding are my shores in fragrant *hinahina.*
We call upon you—oh, give an answer;
  Molokini endures the foam of the sea.
Famed is Oahu for her *ʻilima,*
  Like a feather cape adorning the shoulders.
Famed is Kauai for *mokihana,*
  Lauaʻe of Makana, garden of my homeland.
Shells of Niihau, where are you hiding?
  O pearls of the sea, show forth your beauty.
Now my story is thus completed—
  O garlands of Hawaii, waken to our song.
And now I sing again, my song is over,
  Hiiaka of the sea, beloved one of Pele.

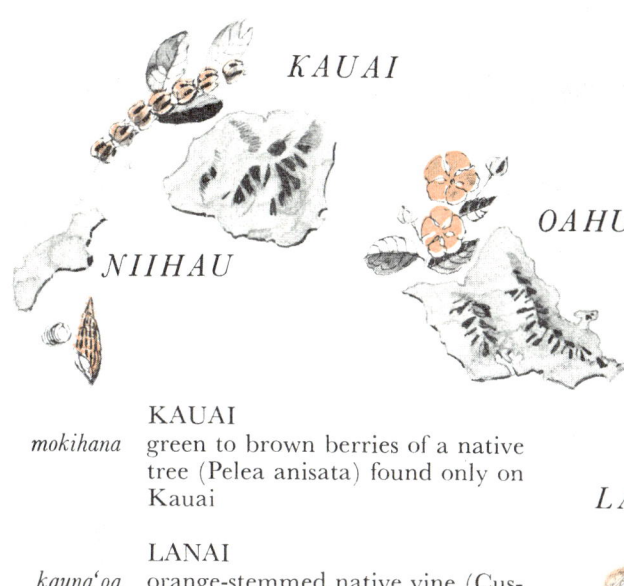

KAUAI
mokihana green to brown berries of a native tree (Pelea anisata) found only on Kauai

LANAI
kaunaʻoa orange-stemmed native vine (Cuscuta sandwichiana) of the morning-glory family; the stems are strung on leis

MAUI
roselani the common small red rose, now substituted for the pink rose; also called *lokelani*

MOLOKAI
kukui silvery leaves and small white flowers of the candlenut tree (Aleurite moluccana)

NIIHAU
pupu small shells

OAHU
ilima small, delicate yellow or orange, greenish or dull red flowers growing on shrubs (Sida); about five hundred blossoms needed for one lei

HAWAII
lehua flowers, usually red, of the *ohiʻa* tree (Metrosideros macropus)

KAHOOLAWE
hinahina a low-spreading beach plant (Heliotropium anomalum) with narrow, clustered, silvery leaves and small, white, fragrant flowers

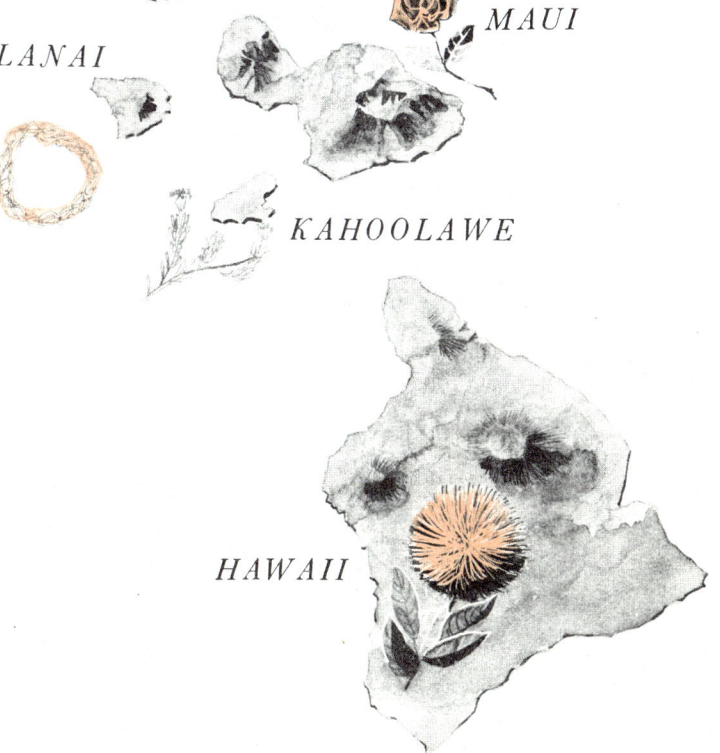

KU'U IPO I KA HE'E PU'EONE
My Sweetheart Surfing

HAWAII

This love song, attributed to Princess Likelike (1851–87), is another example of the *himeni,* with its sixteen-bar verse and sixteen-bar chorus. The composer may have had in mind the ancient Hawaiian custom of chants created in honor of famous surfing chiefs. It should be performed slowly and with personal sentiment. The chorus is presented in a simple two-part arrangement, which may be sung by high and low voices as a duet.

ATTRIB. TO PRINCESS LIKELIKE; ENG. AFTER WM. MEINECKE

ATTRIBUTED TO PRINCESS LIKELIKE

G C G D7
p
Ku-ʻu i - po i ka he -ʻe pu-ʻe - o - - - ne, Me ke ka - i ne-he
Proud-ly glid-ing e-ver shore-ward on the surf - - board, My sweet - heart
G C
i ka ʻi - li - ʻi - - li, Ni-po a - ku i-la - i - la ka ma-
rides the waves so free, Mur-m'ring peb - bles whis-p'ring with the
G D7 G
na - - ʻo, U-a ki-li-ʻo-pu ma - ua i ka na - he - - le.
o - - cean, Of love we share be-side the sea.

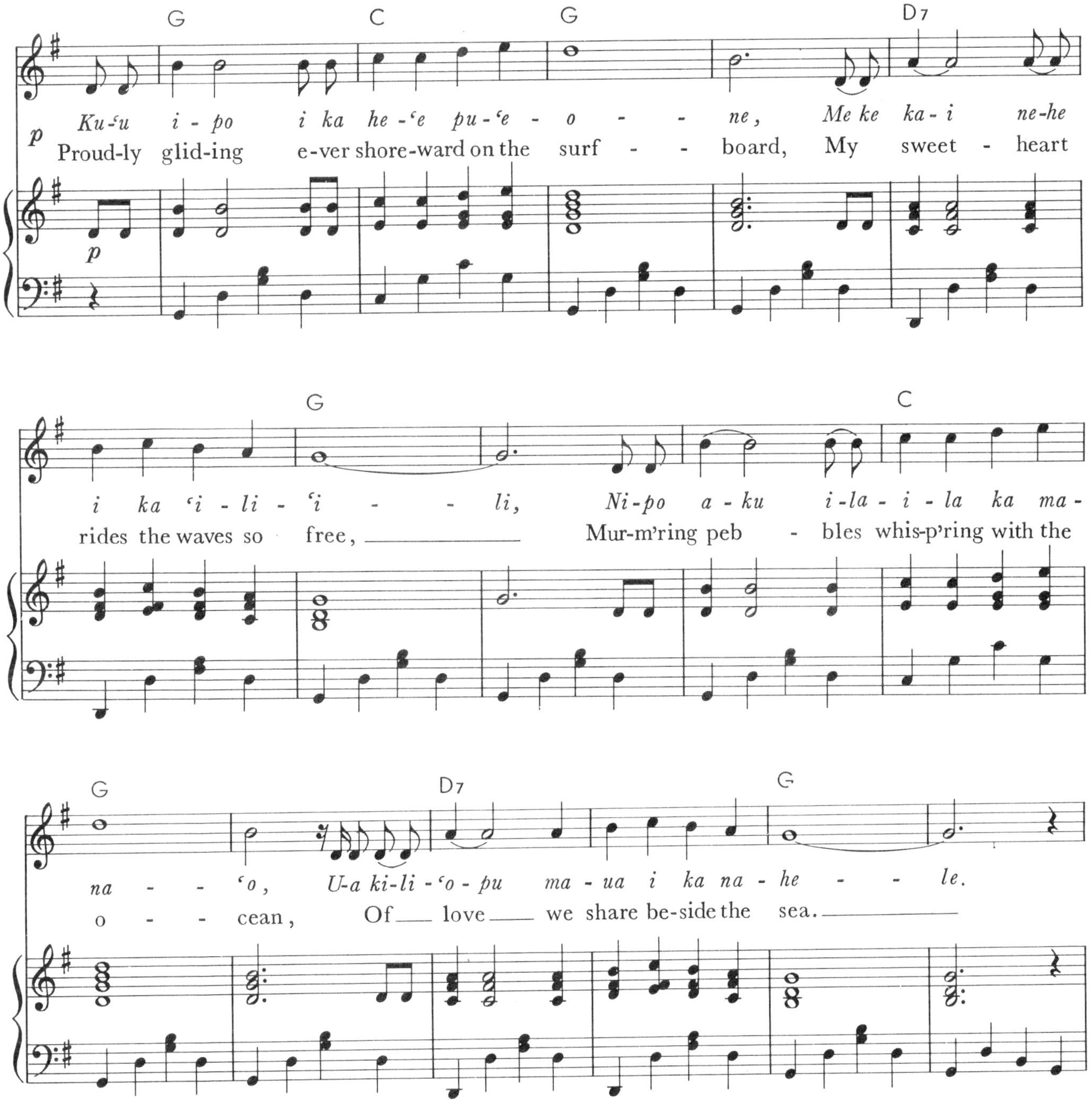

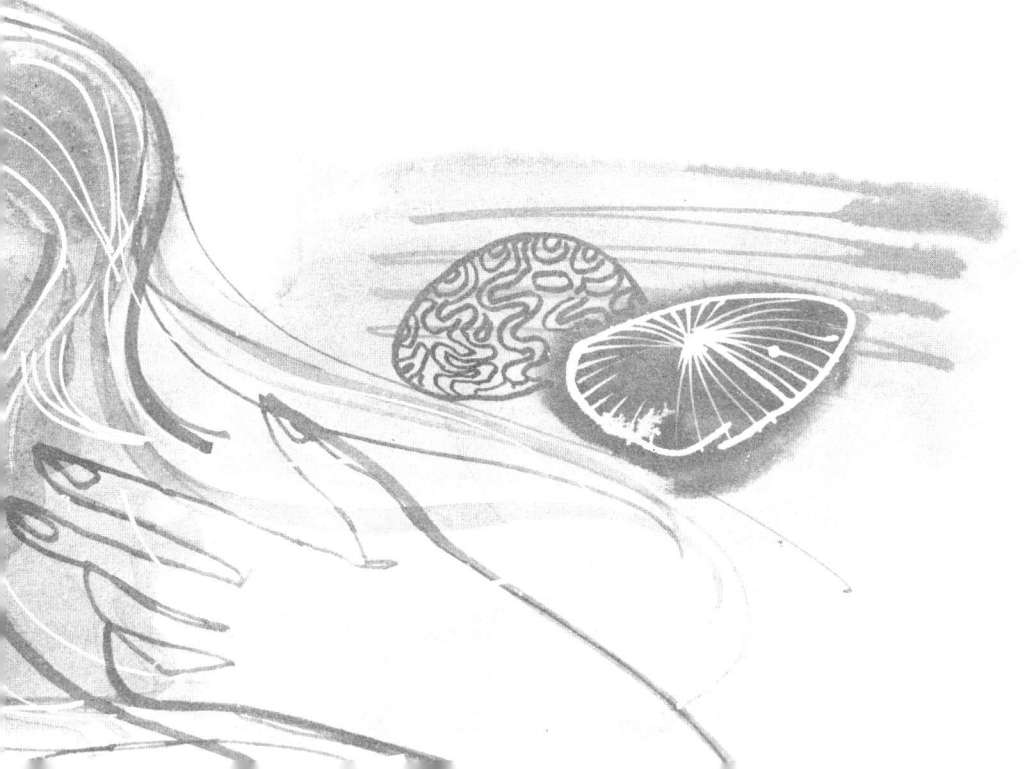

MAKALAPUA
The Opening Flower
HAWAII

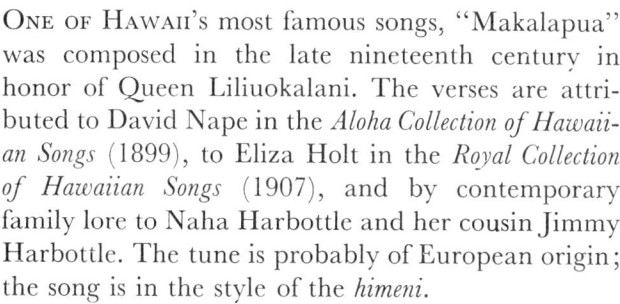

ONE OF HAWAII's most famous songs, "Makalapua" was composed in the late nineteenth century in honor of Queen Liliuokalani. The verses are attributed to David Nape in the *Aloha Collection of Hawaiian Songs* (1899), to Eliza Holt in the *Royal Collection of Hawaiian Songs* (1907), and by contemporary family lore to Naha Harbottle and her cousin Jimmy Harbottle. The tune is probably of European origin; the song is in the style of the *himeni*.

Many Hawaiian names were commemorative of Hawaiian royalty. Such was the case with the names of the queen whose mother's aunt, Kinau, suffered from an illness of the eyes. The child was named Kamakaeha Liliuokalani Lolokulani, meaning "burning eyes with tears pouring down her cheeks like rain." Liliuokalani grew up to be a famous queen; she loved and was identified with the evergreen mountain loveliness of the islands.

Maunahele, the place mentioned in the song, was the name of the verdant gardens that lay in the cool shadow of the famous *pali* (cliff) on the windward side of Oahu; these gardens were sacred to Lia, the mountain goddess of flowers, and it was here that Queen Liliuokalani composed some of her famous songs. At the queen's death, in 1917, this song was sung as her funeral dirge at every change in the watch over her bier.

GLOSSARY: *Kamani,* a tree (Calophyllum inophyllum) native to the islands, bearing edible nuts like almonds and very fragrant blossoms. *Ti,* a very useful indigenous plant (Cordyline terminalis) whose large, smooth, green leaves are used in the cooking of Hawaiian foods, for thatching houses, and for making hula skirts; when cooked their fibrous roots provided the Hawaiian child a natural sweet candy, and when fermented the roots produced an intoxicating beverage.

DISPUTED; ENG. AFTER MARY K. PUKUI   AUTHORSHIP DISPUTED

O ma-ka-la-pu-a u-lu ma-hi-e-hi-e,____ O ka le-i
The o-p'ning flow'r in____ love-li-ness grow-ing,____ The __ lei

2 *Ha'iha'i pua kamani pauku pua ki,*
I lei no 'owehiwehi no ka wahine,
E walea ai ka waokele,
I ka liko i o Maunahele.
  CHORUS

The *kamani* leaves entwined with the *ti* flower,
A lei to beautify Liliu fair,
One who loves the beauteous and fragrant uplands,
Where bud the flowers at Maunahele.
  CHORUS

Music of Polynesia 25

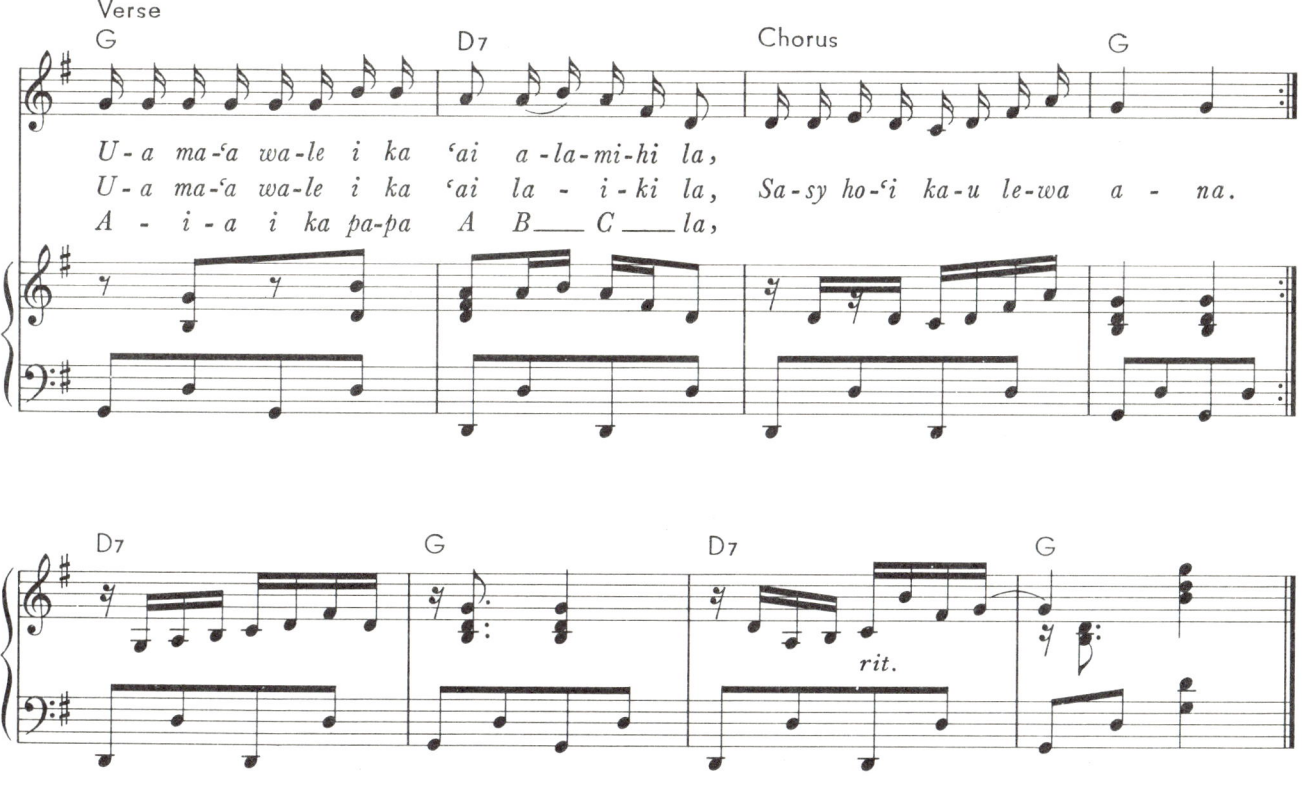

4 *Kaikamahine no Waialae la,*
  Sasy ho'i kau lewa ana;
  Ua ma'a wale i ke kau ekake la,
  Sasy ho'i kau lewa ana.

5 *Ha'ina ia mai ana kapuana la,*
  Sasy ho'i kau lewa ana;
  Ua ma'a wale i ke kau ekake la,
  Sasy ho'i kau lewa ana.

IN THE NINETEENTH CENTURY, Portuguese immigrants to Hawaii brought with them the guitar and what is now known as the ukulele. In the hands of the musically gifted Hawaiians, a singular style of playing developed for these instruments embodying the soft and hospitable mood of the islands. With the guitar this style became known as slack-key ("loosning the strings"). The strings are tuned to a single chord, usually G major; the thumb plucks the bass strings to produce tonic, dominant, and sub-dominant harmonies somewhat similar to the Alberti bass while the forefinger evokes the elusive melody with sliding and unplucked tones on the upper strings. The piano accompaniment given here is an approximation of this slack-key style.

For further information about this hula-form song, see the notes to "I Went to Hilo" (page 32).

A literal translation of the first verse would go something like this: "A little girl from Iwilei does a sassy hula; she eats the brown crab—and does a sassy hula." Succeeding verses, using the same refrain, tell about the girl from Kapalama, eating rice; from Kakaako, learning her ABC's; and from Waialae, riding a donkey. The final verse: "Now my story is concluded. She does a sassy hula; she rides a donkey —and does a sassy hula." The places mentioned are all in Honolulu. Each action ascribed to the girl is intended as a slur against her background, but she always emerges the victor with her sassy hula.

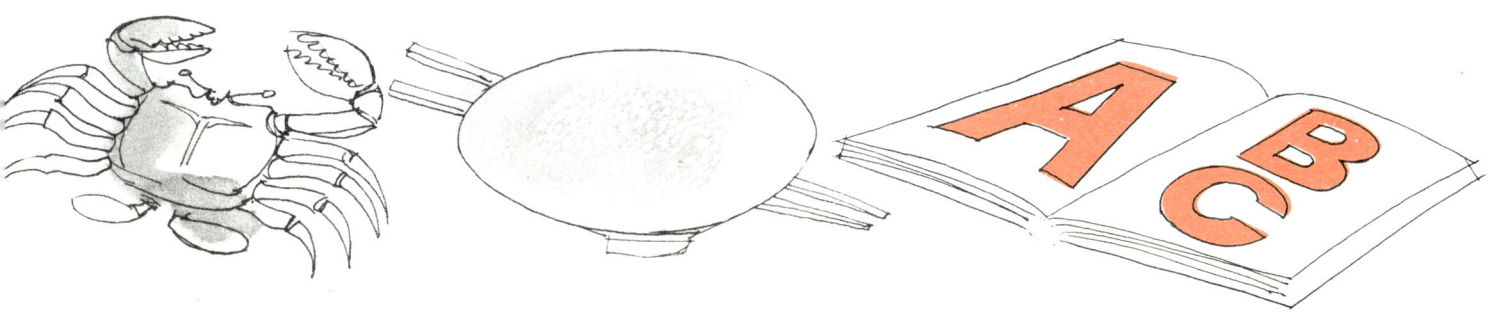

KILAKILA NA ROUGHRIDER
Famed Are the Roughriders

HAWAII

This spirited song, in the fast-hula style, is well known on the island of Hawaii, home of the famous roughriding Hawaiian cowboys. In the 1840's Mexican cowboys were brought to the Hawaiian islands and became known as *paniola,* the Hawaiian pronunciation of the word Spaniard. Since then all cowboys are called *paniola* in Hawaiian, no matter what their race, but are equally well known under their English name of roughriders. The original *paniola* rode the plains of Waimea on Hawaii and started a tradition that has made song and legend ring with the sound of their spurs and their shouts.

The literal meaning of the repeated couplet of the chorus is: "The aching, tingling in the heart," but singable English lyrics have been substituted in this version.

Glossary: *Kipuʻupuʻu,* the name given the chilly rains that occasionally sweep across the plains of Waimea bringing to nearly sea level the cooler air from the heights of Mauna Kea and Mauna Loa, Hawaii's towering volcanoes. One of King Kamehameha's finest runners took the name, thus spreading the fame of Waimea's rains far and wide.

ANON.; ENG. AFTER MARY K. PUKUI   ANON.; AS SUNG BY KAREN PERKINS

Folk Songs Hawaii Sings

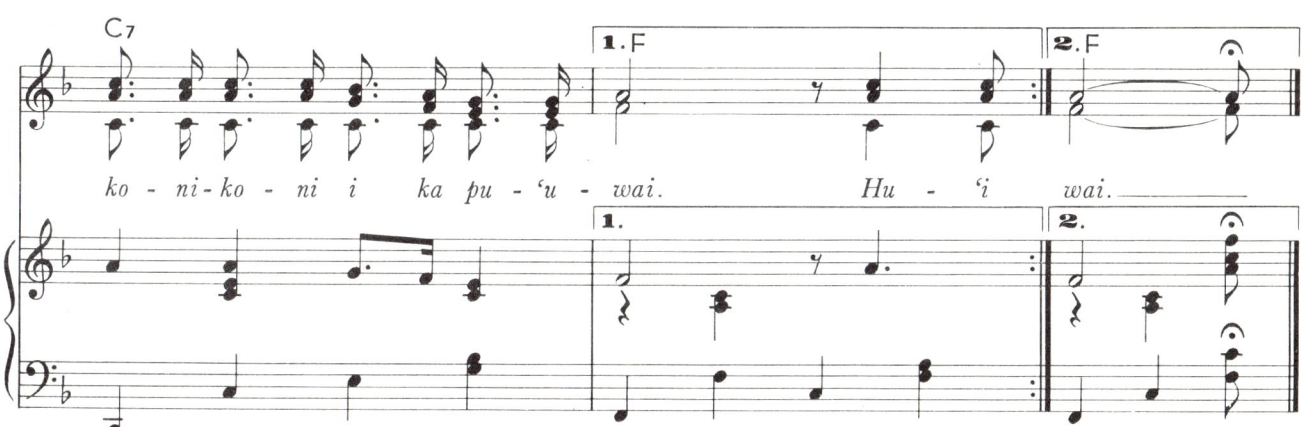

1 *Kilakila na* roughrider,
 Me ka ua Kipuʻupuʻu,
 Me ka nani o Puu Kalani,
 Me ka hae o ka lanakila.

CHORUS: *Huʻi e huʻi eha!*
 Huʻi konikoni i ka puʻuwai;
 Huʻi e huʻi EHA!
 Huʻi konikoni i ka puʻuwai.

2 *ʻAkahi hoʻi au a ʻike maka,*
 Na roughrider ka hulu ʻekahi;
 Inu ana i ka wai aniani,
 E maʻu i ka puʻu ke moni.

 CHORUS

As famed are the roughriders
As the rain *Kipuʻupuʻu,*
And the beauty of Puu Kalani
Carrying the banner of vict'ry.

 Hey! Roughriders!
 Ride on, Hawaiian cowboys!
 Hey-ya, EHA!
 Carrying the banner of vict'ry.

Here come the roughriders,
Brave Hawaiian cowboys;
They drink from sparkling waters
On the plains of Waimea.

 CHORUS

3 *Hanohano wale na* cowboy,
 E makuʻu noho i ka lio;
 Halena pono ʻoe i (ke) kaula ʻili,
 I ka lae o ka pipi ʻahiu.

 CHORUS

Oh, handsome are the cowboys,
Proudly mounting their horses;
Pull taut now your lassos,
Hold the brow of the plunging cattle.

 CHORUS

Music of Polynesia

KA INUWAI
The Thirsty Winds of Kohala

HAWAII

A BEAUTIFUL SONG attributed to David Nape, famous songwriter of the turn of the century, this sings of the "drink-water" (*inuwai*) winds that parch Kohala on the island of Hawaii. Representative of the *himeni* form, this may be sung as a solo or solo with chorus. The two upper voices of the chorus may be sung as a duet for high and low voices. The lyrics, attributed to William Sheldon, mention three places—Kohala, Niulii, and Hapuu. The "three clouds" is a reference to three sisters, one of whom was evidently the poet's sweetheart. His view of her home was hidden by the *hala* (pandanus) grove of Hapuu.

ATTRIB. TO WM. SHELDON; ENG. AFTER MARY K. PUKUI   ATTRIB. TO DAVID NAPE

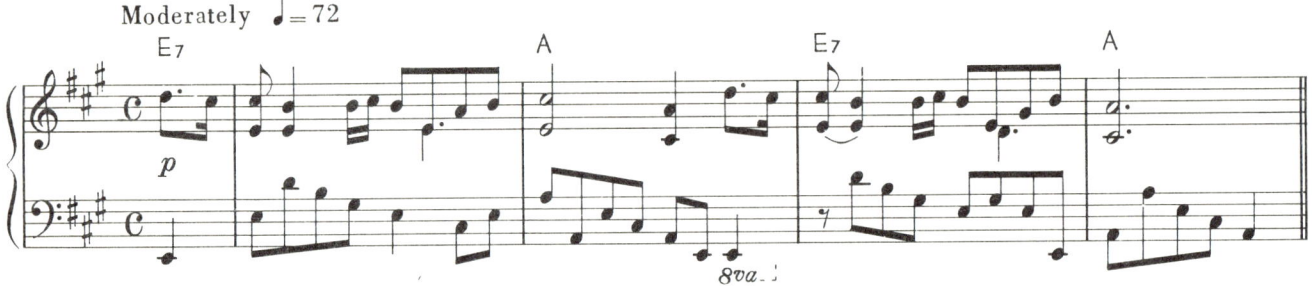

Ma-i-ka-'i ka ma-ka-ni o Ko-ha - - la, 'I-ke
E-ver blowing, the breez-es of Ko-ha - - la, Thirs-ty

'i a e ke I-nu-wa-i._____ O ka wai no i - a po-no ka
wind whose name is I-nu-wa-i._____ O the waters life-giv-ing to all

30 *Folk Songs Hawaii Sings*

2 *Nani wale Niuliʻi hakela i ka laʻi,*   Calm and peaceful the lovely Niulii,
   ʻEkolu ʻopua i hiki mai;   Moving softly, three clouds are coming hither;
   ʻAlai ia mai e ka ulu hala,   Beyond the peaceful groves of *hala*,
   Nalo wale ka luna o Hapuʻu.   Lies hidden the summit of Hapuu.

   CHORUS   CHORUS

I Went to Hilo

HAWAII

Both "Sassy" and "I Went to Hilo" are hula songs. "Sassy" was first published in 1898, probably having been well known for some time before, while "I Went to Hilo" became popular during the early 1900's.

The hula-song form is a union of the strophic couplets of the ancient *mele hula* (a chant to accompany dancing, usually with gourd or drum accompaniment) with the harmony, scale tones, and cadences of Western music. Such songs are also known as *hapa haole* (half-white).

An explanation of the "leis of the Islands" is on pg. 19.

Glossary: *Hilo,* the largest city on the island of Hawaii. *Maui,* one of the main islands, on which is the large extinct volcano *Haleakala. Oahu,* the island on which Honolulu, the Islands' largest city, is located. *Kauai,* another of the main islands, site of Mt. *Waialeale,* the wettest spot on earth. *Ha'ina ia mai ana ka puana,* see the glossary, page 17.

ANONYMOUS — ANONYMOUS

In hula tempo ♩ = about 80

Melody in upper part

1. Hi - lo, the vol - ca - no.
I went to 2. Mau - i, To see Ha-le-a-ka-la. I met my
3. O-a-hu, Ho-no-lu - lu.

Folk Songs Hawaii Sings

4 I went to Kauai
   To see Waialeale.
   I met my Hawaiian maid;
   She presented lei *mokihana*.

5 *Ha'ina ia mai
   Ana ka puana.*
   I met my Hawaiian maid;
   She presented leis of the Islands.

Music of Polynesia 33

SIVA SIVA MAIA
Come, Dance
SAMOA

ANON.; AS SUNG BY TAVITA
ANONYMOUS

Fast ♩ = 112

1. Tei - ne tei - ne
2. A - ta a - ta mai - a,
3. & 4. Si - va si - va

34 *Folk Songs Hawaii Sings*

Like most other islanders of the Pacific, the Samoans are a dance-loving people. In the old days dances were performed on most formal and special occasions—to honor royalty, to prepare for war or to practice arts of self-defense, to celebrate fishing, planting, and harvesting activities, and to accompany village festivals. Some of the old dances still remain and are performed today. Among the popular dances of recent times, like the present example, is the informal social dancing accompanied by singing and the playing of guitars, ukuleles, and drums.

The melody of "Come, Dance" shows the influence of Western tonality. Samoan music is often quite spirited and generally faster than the corresponding music of Hawaii. Soon after contact with Western music, especially the missionary hymns, the Samoans developed great ability in spontaneous part singing.

In the accompanying arrangement, the left-hand figure is meant to suggest a fast drum pattern. The Samoan word *teine* is pronounced *teng-a*.

Tavita has supplied the following literal translation: "Come, shake; come, shake—time for fun and singing—shake, everybody, shake up and down." The word "shake" changes to "laugh" in the second verse and to "dance" in the third.

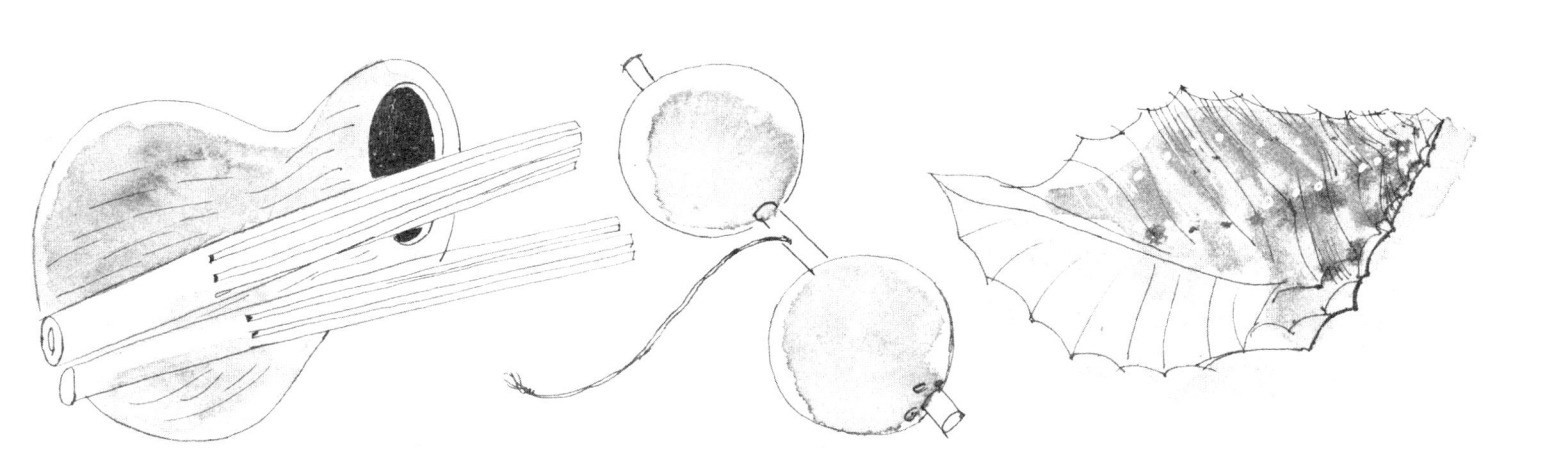

ATU LANGOTO
The Bonito Leap
UVEA

Uvea (Wallis Island) lies roughly west of Samoa and north of Fiji in the western Pacific. Its people, numbering almost five thousand, can be described as western Polynesian.

"The Bonito Leap" is an ancient song used to accompany the *soamoko,* a type of indoor dancing performed at family festivals and on informal social occasions. The songs of these dances consist of little couplets repeated with increasing tempo until singers and dancers grow weary. The singers are a separate chorus grouped about a rolled mat which is beaten with sticks as an accompaniment. First the beating begins, quite slowly, and then the singing begins. The tempo accelerates gradually to a speed limited only by the energy of the singers and dancers. The final note is prolonged, then falls away in a trailing cadence (which is indicated in the vocal score by the curved arrows). Dancers and spectators often accompany the singing with clapping of hands together and on various parts of the body—the shoulders, thighs, face, etc. Several varieties of sound can thus be produced, such as the *pate* (hands clapped flat) and the *po* (hands cupped).

This song was collected by E. G. Burrows, who gives this literal translation: "The bonito fall like the panadanus petal. Fish for bonito!" These words have been expanded and freely adapted to produce four singable English verses.

ANON.; ENG. AFTER E. G. BURROWS ANONYMOUS

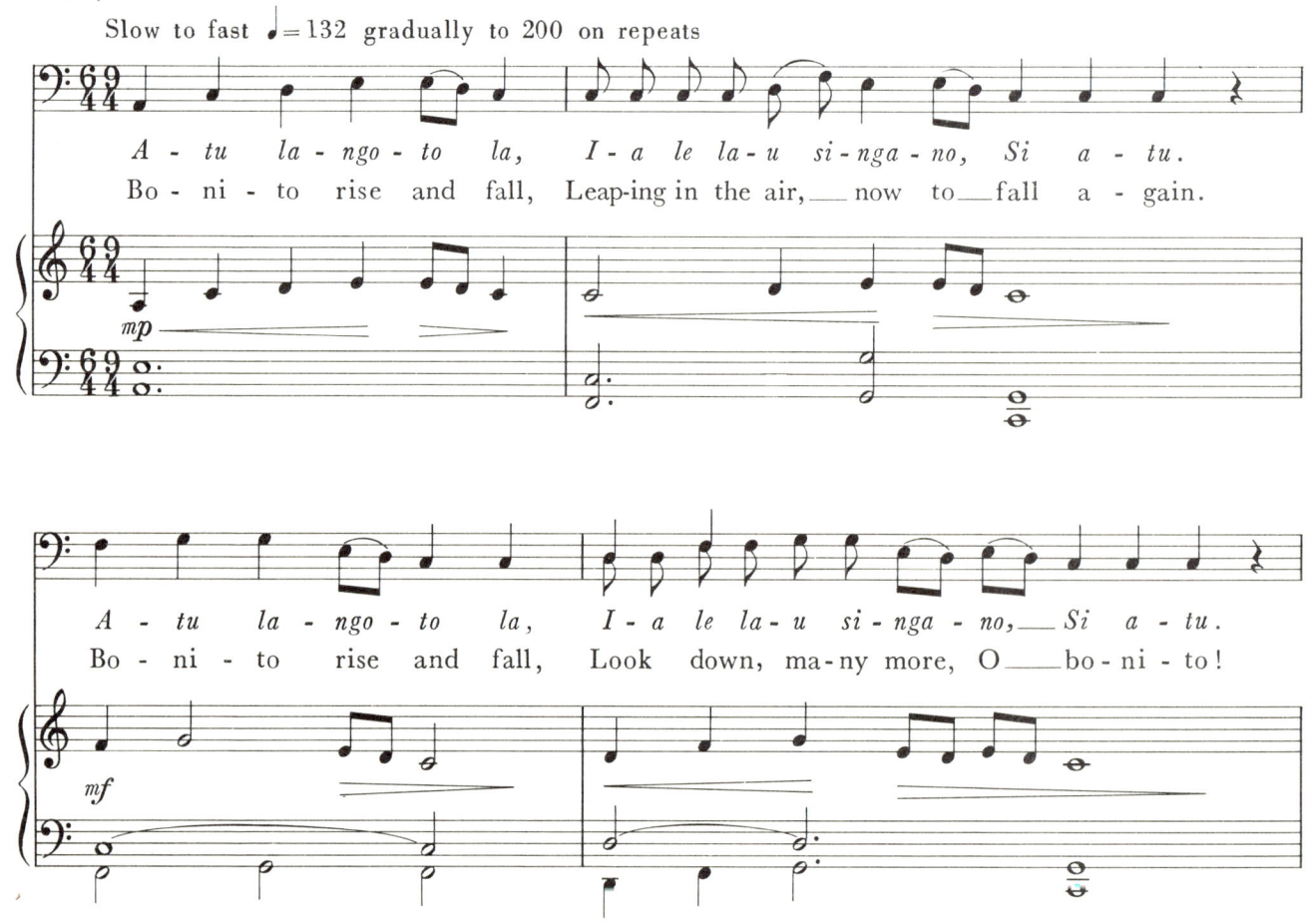

Slow to fast ♩=132 gradually to 200 on repeats

A - tu la - ngo - to la, I - a le la - u si - nga - no, Si a - tu.
Bo - ni - to rise and fall, Leap-ing in the air,— now to— fall a - gain.

A - tu la - ngo - to la, I - a le la - u si - nga - no,— Si a - tu.
Bo - ni - to rise and fall, Look down, ma-ny more, O— bo - ni - to!

Folk Songs Hawaii Sings

A - tu la - ngo - to la, I - a le la - u si - nga - no, Si a - tu.
Bo - ni - to rise and fall, Like the leaves of pan - dan - us.

last time

A - tu la - ngo - to la, I - a le la - u si - nga - no, Si a - tu, Si a - tu uh!
Now we catch bo - ni - to, Throw the hook, pull taut, O bo - ni - to. O bo - ni - to!

p

ad lib.

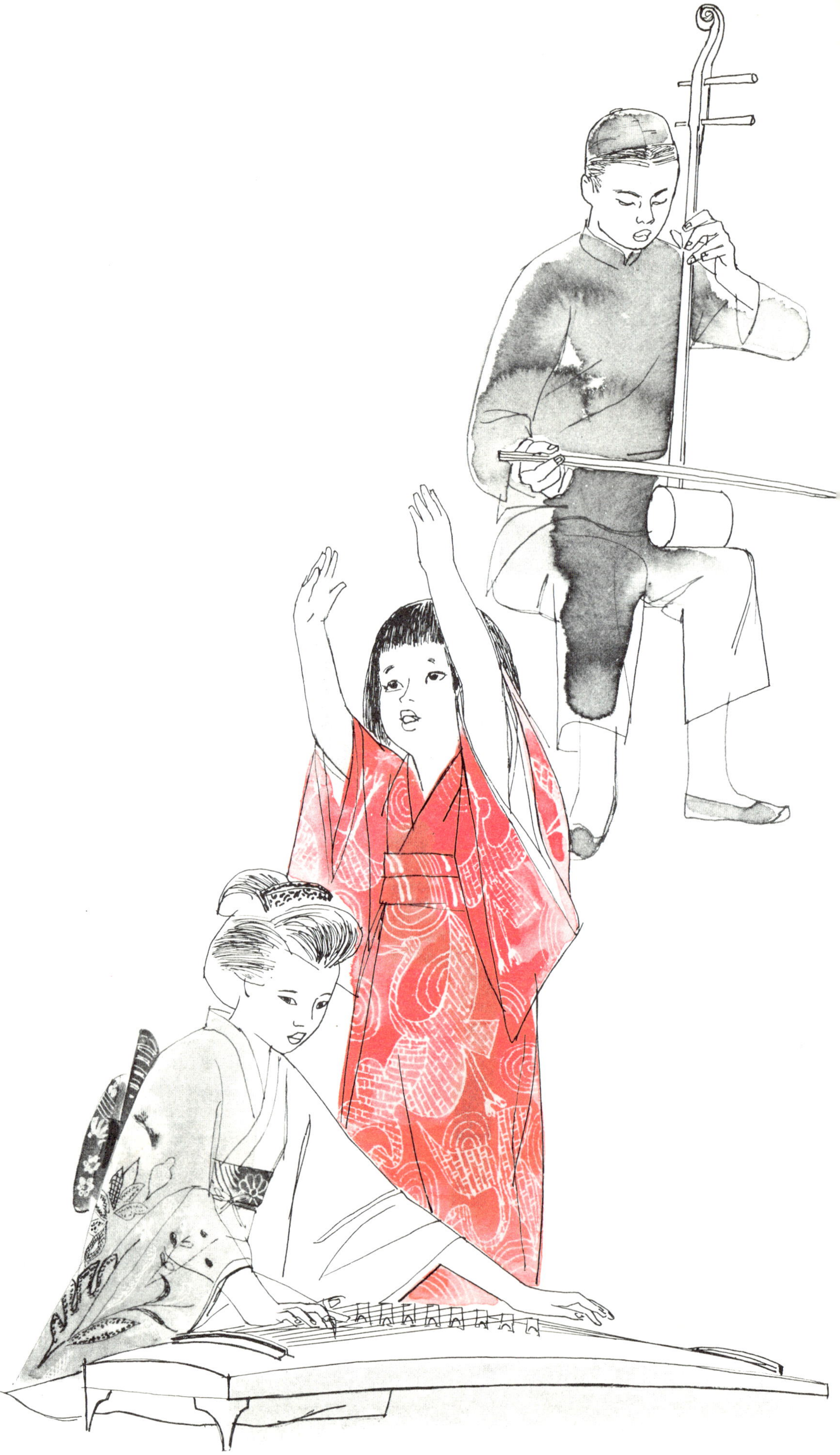

MUSIC OF ASIA

THE VAST FIELD OF ASIAN MUSIC would be impossible to summarize even in one book. Each nation has many distinctive geographical and historical traditions. There are, however, several interesting features which are shared in common to one degree or another that may help to make the music of these many nations more understandable. Inasmuch as the Asian folk songs in this volume reflect the heritage of the people of Hawaii who came in significant numbers from Japan, the Ryukyus, Korea, China, and the Philippines, the term Asian here refers to these areas but does not include India or the rest of Asia.

There are two main cleavages in the music of Asia. The first distinguishes folk music from court music; and the second separates music of pre-European from post-European contact.

Court music was an art practiced and heard only by a guarded lineage of nobility, courtiers, and practitioners. Although stylistic differences mark various periods and localities, the essential form and content of this traditional, classical art have remained unchanged for centuries. Even in modern Japan, for example, the imperial court musicians still perform music as it was heard centuries ago, and many of the performers trace their professional lineage back for hundreds of years. The texts of some of these classical vocal works are often rendered in such archaic poetry that even the performers may not understand them.

The peasantry did not have schools, libraries, or leisure in which to institutionalize their art. The hardships and brief pleasures of life were expressed and recorded in informal balladry, puppetry, song, and dance. The fluid folk arts were imbued with earthy humor and punctuated with vigorous rhythms abstracted from daily tasks. Free-swinging melodies contrasted with the tightly woven melodic texture of court music. In respect to tempi, subject matter, and audiences, the folk music of Japan, Korea, and China has more in common than each has with its respective national court music.

Urbanization and growing industrialization in the late nineteenth and early twentieth centuries weakened the traditional agrarian village life which had cradled much of Asian folk art. As was the case with industry and commerce, culture patterns became increasingly infused with forms and techniques of Western origin, a trend greatly magnified during and after World War II.

In Japan, for example, schools began teaching Western and Westernized songs in place of those of their own tradition. Native Japanese folk songs dropped out of the song books, and composers such as Ryutaro Hirota (see page 44) composed a wholly new children's song literature combining Western tonality and form with the Asian pentatonic scale and Japanese language. There is, however, a definite movement to revive native folklore and folk song in Japanese schools.

The free spirit of Korean folk music and dancing is distinctive. Its popularity extends through nearly all levels of society. This is interesting in view of the fact that Korea has had to wage a ceaseless struggle for national independence during practically its entire history. Whereas duple time predominates in neighboring Japanese and Chinese folk music, triple time is more prevalent in Korean folk music.

Folk music and dance in China have attained long-overdue recognition through extensive collecting, collating, and study projects. Folk performing groups flourish, and amateur concerts are frequent in factory and field. There is also a scholarly interest in mastering Western techniques, as there is in other Asian countries as well. Many traditional Chinese folk songs may be heard in choral and orchestral settings in new forms that unite native with Western traditions.

In the Philippines there is a movement to re-establish a national art that is aboriginal in character. The exponents of this movement are facing great difficulties in that three hundred years of Spanish domination all but obliterated the pre-European arts. A recent field-research project by the Silliman University Foundation for Musical Research has resulted in the publication of several volumes of folk songs that appear to reflect the thorough Hispanization of Filipino culture. The rhythms, forms, and melodic designs are almost uniformly of Spanish origin. Nonetheless, there are still distinctively Filipino qualities that shine through the European formalities.

Notwithstanding the distance and time separating many modern Hawaiians from their ancestral Asian homelands, most, if not all, of the main characteristics of Asian folk music are still found today among the people of Hawaii.

Music of Asia

SAKURA
Cherry Blossoms
JAPAN

ANONYMOUS — ANONYMOUS

Slowly ♩ = 69

1. Sa - ku - ra, sa - ku - ra, Ya - yo - i no so - ra wa,
2. Sa - i - ta sa - ku - ra Ha - na mi - te mo - do - ro,

Mi - wa - ta - su ka - gi - ri, Ka - su - mi ka ku - mo ka,
Yo - shi - no wa sa - ku - ra, Ta - tsu - ta wa mi - do - ri,

42 *Folk Songs Hawaii Sings*

Ni - o - i zo i - zu - ru, I - za ya, i - za ya,
Ka - ra - sa - ki no ma - tsu, To - ki wa, to - ki wa,

Slower

Mi____ ni yu ka - - n.
I - - za yu ka -

Optional cadenza in *koto* style

pp fast and lightly   *cresc.*

THIS IS AN EXAMPLE of the studied form of court poetry and music of ancient Japan. The first verse, in a literal translation by Grace Saito, goes: "Cherry blossoms! Cherry blossoms! In the March sky as far as one can see, like mist, like clouds . . . Their fragrance is everywhere. Come, come, let's go and see." This verse, containing an element of mysticism, was written in the nineteenth century and is now probably better known than the second, which is the older text. The second verse is also a more direct and simple concept: "After seeing the full-blown blossoms let's return home. It's Yoshino for cherry blossoms, Tatsuta for maple leaves, and Karasaki for pine trees. Always and always let's go."

The cherry blossom is the national flower of Japan. In spring the countryside glows with the breathtaking beauty of countless pink and white cherry blossoms. The three places named in the second verse are famed for their natural beauty, and frequent outings are made to them.

In Japan the song is often accompanied on the *koto* with a delicate melodically imitative design.

Music of Asia

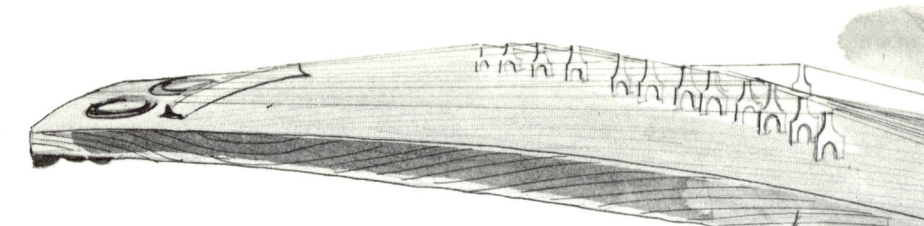

ON-KOTO
Honorable Koto
JAPAN

THIS GOOD-HUMORED SONG was popular in Japan in the nineteenth century and in 1839 was even incorporated by an eminent composer, Rokuo Kineya, into a larger work entitled "Comic Lion Dance." It is a fine song by which to learn the names of several Japanese musical instruments.

ANON.; ENG. AFTER S. TSUGAWA
ANONYMOUS
With spirit ♩=100

On ko-to, ko-to, ko-to, choi-to sha-mi-yo, Choi-to shi-ta ha-u-ta de choi-to tsu-zu-mi. To-tchi-ri o-ka-wa

On ko-to, ko-to ko-to, and the sha-mi-sen, Sing a cheer-ful lit-tle song and play the small hand drum. Sing then and beat the hand drum

44 *Folk Songs Hawaii Sings*

GLOSSARY: *Koto,* a 13-string horizontal harp. *Shamisen,* a 3-string banjo-like instrument; here abbreviated to *shami*. *Tsuzumi,* a small double-ended drum usually held over the shoulder or at the knee; often called *ko-tsuzumi* to distinguish it from a larger drum. *Taiko,* a large standing drum. *Okawa,* a large hand drum. *Kokyu,* a bowed viol. *Fue,* a short bamboo flute. *Hauta,* a chansonnette. *Totchiriton Bushi,* a song popular in the early nineteenth century.

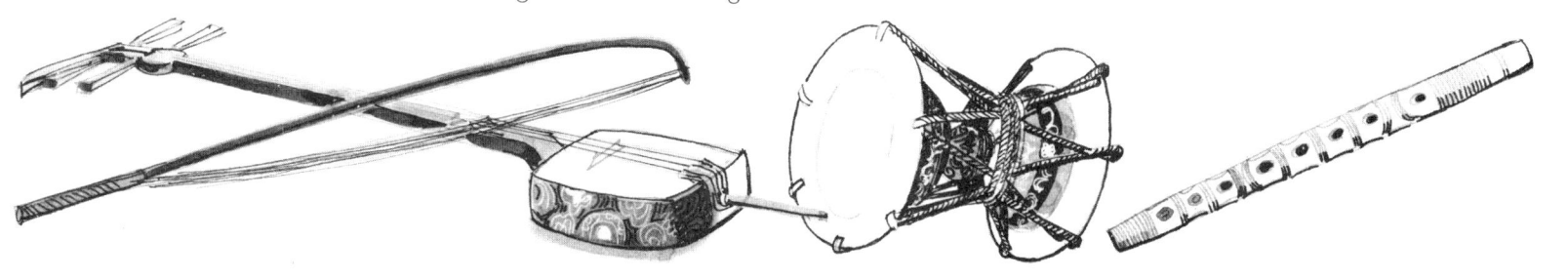

KISO BUSHI
Song of Kiso

JAPAN

This is a song of the hardy woodcutters and lumberjacks of the Kiso region in central Honshu, the largest of Japan's main islands. Kiso is high in the mountains and is quite cool even in summer.

This song has been recorded by many of Japan's best folk and popular singers, and as with most folk songs there are many versions of both melody and lyrics. It is often used to accompany Bon Festival dancing.

The months of July and August are the Bon Festival season in Japan, a time when village festivals are held to commemorate good deeds and to remember one's forefathers. The people gather on specified nights to dance for hours in a circle around the *yagura,* a tall wooden platform for the drummers, flutists, singers, and *shamisen* players. The dance steps are simple so young and old alike can participate. The dancers, each dancing individually in the circle, move with gracefully active motions, always an extra step more forward than the two or three steps taken backward and to the side, so that the circle moves slowly around the *yagura.* The dancing and the music take their tempo from a huge drum, called *o-daiko,* played by one or more players. The drumming is a vigorous art of body movement. The Bon music rhythms are energetic and the melodies alive and filled with resources. Thus the sound of the Bon drums and the shrilling flutes echo throughout the village and across the field, irresistably drawing all out of their homes.

The Bon tradition has been well established in Hawaii for over a generation, with various groups championing the songs and rhythms of their homeland localities, such as Niigata, Fukushima, and other Japanese cities and prefectures. Fukushima Prefecture gives rise to the Kiso River, used for logging, where this "Song of Kiso" originated, near the famous Mt. Ontake.

The phrases *nanjara hoi* and *yoi yoi yoi* are mere exclamations, without meaning. The *yoi yoi yoi* refrain is generally joined in by everyone, dancers, singers, and onlookers alike. Omitting the refrain, the second and third verses, in literal translation by Masato Matsumoto, say: "2. Winter clothes, boatman, winter clothes we'd like to give you—and socks to keep you warm. 3. Winter clothes, boatman, how can one afford—to give winter clothes?"

ANON.; ENG. AFTER MASATO MATSUMOTO   ANONYMOUS

46 Folk Songs Hawaii Sings

na-ka-no-ri-sa-n, Ki-so no On-ta-ke-san wa? Nan-ja-ra hoi! Na-tsu de-mo
going down the riv-er, Say how is On-ta-ke-san? Nan-ja-ra hoi! E-ven the sum-

sa-mu-i, Yoi yoi yoi! Yoi yoi yoi no yoi yoi yoi! yoi yoi yoi!
mer's cold, Yoi yoi yoi! Yoi yoi yoi no yoi yoi yoi! yoi yoi yoi!

2 *Awase na nakanori-san,*
  Awase yarita ya—
  Nanjara hoi!
  Tabi o soete.
  Yoi yoi yoi!
  Yoi yoi yoi no yoi yoi yoi!

3 *Awase na nakanori-san,*
  Awase bakari wa—
  Nanjara hoi!
  Yarare mo semai.
  Yoi yoi yoi!
  Yoi yoi yoi no yoi yoi yoi!

HIRAITA
It's Open!
JAPAN

MANY CHILDREN attending Japanese language school in Hawaii learn this song, sometimes to a modernized version of the melody. The older version is presented here because it familiarizes us with the sound of the ancient scale and its use of half-tone intervals.

When children sing the song they form a circle. As the flower opens, the performers' arms sweep up and out and the circle widens. When the flower closes, the circle contracts as arms and bowed heads simulate the closing petals.

The lotus plant is of the water-lily family; its lovely white to rose-colored flower opens in the morning, closes that night, and opens again the next morning. The petals begin to drop off the evening of the second day. Although generally associated with the Orient, many types of lotuses are found in the United States.

In Asia the lotus has symbolic Buddhistic meaning. Its wheel-like shape represents the concept of a perpetual cycle of existence. And in Europe such composers as Schumann and Franz wrote compositions inspired by the flower's beauty.

The lyrics express the changeableness of nature. Grace Saito has provided the following literal translation: "1. It's open, it's open! What flower is open? The lotus flower is open. I thought for a moment it was open; now it's shut tight. 2. It's shut tight, it's shut tight! What flower is shut tight? The lotus flower is shut tight. I thought for a moment it was shut tight; now it's open."

ANONYMOUS ANONYMOUS

Moderately ♩ = 56

1. Hi - rai - ta hi - rai - ta,
2. Tsu - bon - da tsu - bon - da,

Na - n no ha - na ga hi - rai - ta? Ren - ge no ha - na ga hi - rai - ta. Hi - rai - ta to
Na - n no ha - na ga tsu - bon - da? Ren - ge no ha - na ga tsu - bon - da. Tsu - bon - da to

48 *Folk Songs Hawaii Sings*

o - mot-ta - ra   i - tsu no ma   ni ka   tsu - - bo - n - da.
o - mot-ta - ra   i - tsu no ma   ni ka   hi - - ra - i - ta.

Music of Asia 49

KUTSU GA NARU
Sound of Running Feet
JAPAN

This is a Japanese children's song of recent times, composed by Ryutaro Hirota, whose many children's songs are well known in Hawaii as well as in Japan. The melody is pentatonic and avoids the chromatic in-between tones often found in the older folk songs. The open whole-tone intervals provide a rather jocular and outgoing mood which contrasts with the more inward-turning sentiments suggested by chromatic half steps in such older songs as "Cherry Blossoms." The phrase lengths and cadences show the strong influence that has come from Western music.

The song is often given added interest for young singers by having them stamp their feet in time with the music at the words *kutsu ga naru* (literally, "shoes sound," but more freely rendered in our English version as "run, feet, run along"). The piano part imitates in a rather free fashion the Japanese instrumental style, although at the same time employing Western harmony suggested by the form and character of the melody.

KATSURA SHIMIZU; ENG. AFTER MARGARET IIZAKI   RYUTARO HIROTA

O - te - te tsu - na - i - de, No - mi - chi o yu - ke - ba.
Hand in hand, run-ning a-long, Down the wild path we will go.

© Copyright MCMLX by Edward B. Marks Music Corp. Published by arrangement with the Japanese Society of Rights of Authors and Composers. All Rights Reserved. Used by permission of the copyright owners.

Mi - n - na ka - wa - i Ko - to - ri ni nat - te,
Eve - ry one! Let us be lit - tle birds in o - pen fields,

U - ta o u - ta - e - ba Ku - tsu ga na - ru.
Sing - ing our joy - ful songs so run, feet, run, a - long.

Ha - re - ta mi - so - ra ni Ku - tsu ga na - ru.
Clear is the sky of spring so run, feet, run, a -

long.

Music of Asia 51

MENUHAMA BUSHI
Song of Menuhama
OKINAWA

THIS IS THE FIRST of a three-part song cycle that is often sung and danced at parties and social get-togethers on Okinawa. It is followed by *Sakawara Koduchi,* about a flower of beauty that does not bloom, and *Yonabaru Bushi,* which contains the appropriate line, "This is a good party: let it continue until sunrise!" There seems to be no connection between the three songs in subject matter or form except tradition. The first of the three has been selected for inclusion here because of the special beauty of its melody.

The Ryukyuan folk song, popularly accompanied on the *shamisen* or a small drum, or both, differs from that of mainland Japan in its predominately slow and measured tempi and the prevalence of what Western musicians would call a tonal center or tonic in the melodic outline.

The score is given here in unmeasured notation to avoid metrical emphasis implied by the usual Western time signatures and meter. Edward Nakashima's literal translation of the lyrics goes: "1. *Yei, yei,* at Menuhama, at Menuhama along the beaches, a flock of plover is calling *Chiri-chirichi-e.* 2. *Yei, yei,* at Watanji are boats of passage—just by pushing their pounding oars to and fro people come and go. *Chichai.*"

GLOSSARY: *Menuhama* and *Watanji,* coastal place names. *Yei* and *yei-sa,* expressions like tra-la-la without specific meaning.

ANONYMOUS

ANON.; AS SUNG BY ZENKICHI TAMANAHA

Me-nu-ha-ma ni e-ye, Tu-byu-ru sa ha ma chi-du-ri ___ ye-i-sa, Tu-mu yu-bu ku-i ___ wa chi-ri chi-ri-chi, Chi-ri chi-ri-chi-e.

wa-ta-shi bu-ni ku-gu, Tu-mu nu sa ru nu u-tu ka ___ ye-i-sa, Ka-ra-ri ku-ru-ri ku-gi ba'n-ja-i, ___ Chi-cha-i.

LERON, LERON, SINTA
Leron, Leron, My Dear
PHILIPPINES

ANON.; ENG. AFTER AURELIA VIERNES ANONYMOUS

Rubato in good humor ♩=72~76

Le-ron, Le-ron sin-ta, Bu-
ron, Le-ron, my dear, Climbed

ko ng pa-pa-ya, Da la da-la-'y bus-lo, Si-
one pa-pa-ya tree, A bas-ket in his hand, With

sid-lan ng sin-ta. Pag-da-ting sa du lo'y, Na-
love, to fill for me. The high-est branch he gained, It

54 *Folk Songs Hawaii Sings*

A Tagalog children's song, "Leron, Leron, My Dear" is a humorous song with a melody that keeps popping up with different verses from many different islands of the Philippines. The present version is well known in Hawaii.

The people of the Philippines love to harmonize their songs in thirds as arranged here. The upper line is the tune of the song. Sing it with a mixture of mock seriousness and jollity.

Children of Hawaii and the Pacific islands know that the papaya tree is not to be climbed even for its delicious fruit. Its trunk is pithy and porous and the branches are just strong enough to support its melon-sized fruit without a strong wind—let alone an amorous Leron!

Music of Asia 55

MAGTANIM AY DI BIRO
Planting Rice
PHILIPPINES

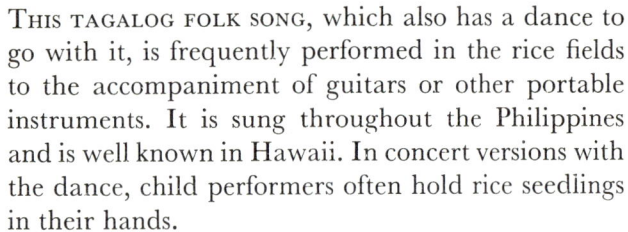

This tagalog folk song, which also has a dance to go with it, is frequently performed in the rice fields to the accompaniment of guitars or other portable instruments. It is sung throughout the Philippines and is well known in Hawaii. In concert versions with the dance, child performers often hold rice seedlings in their hands.

Throughout Asia, rice is usually planted collectively by groups of families, often by an entire village. The rice planters work in long rows thrusting the seedlings into the mud, first to one side, then to the other, and then they step backward to begin a new row. In the Philippines, music is often used to speed up this monotonous stoop-work.

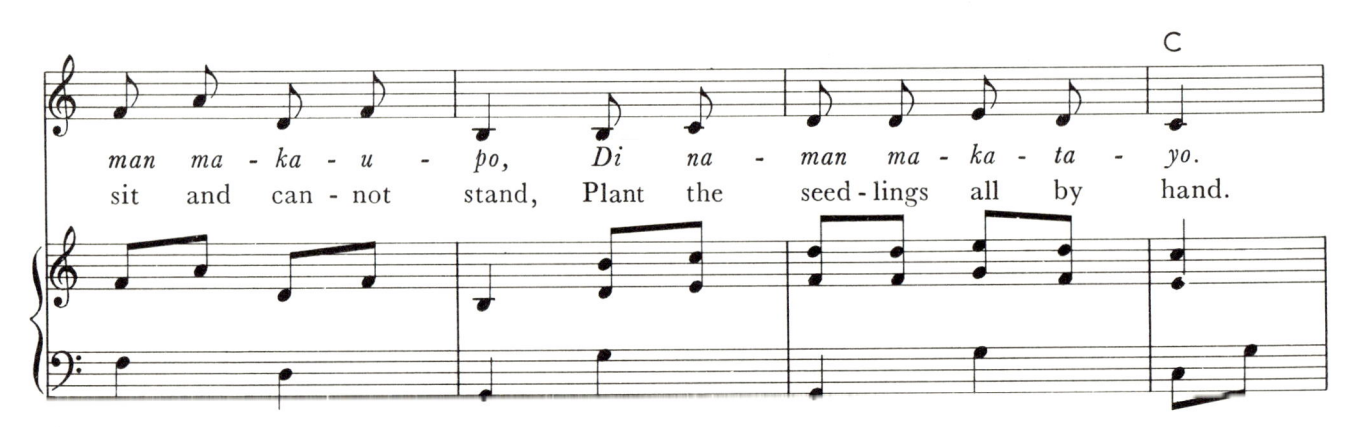

ANON.; ENG. AFTER AURELIA VIERNES

ANONYMOUS

With spirit ♩ = 120

Mag-ta-nim ay di bi-ro, Mag-ha-pon kang na-ka-yu-ko, Di na man ma-ka-u-po, Di na man ma-ka-ta-yo.

Plant-ing rice is ne-ver fun, Work from morn till set of sun, Can-not sit and can-not stand, Plant the seed-lings all by hand.

Folk Songs Hawaii Sings

Chorus

Magtanim di biro, Maghapon nakayuko,
Dinaman makaupo, Dinaman makatayo.

Planting rice is no fun, Work from morn till set of sun,
Cannot sit, Cannot stand, Plant the seedlings all by hand.

BAHAY KUBO
My Nipa Hut
PHILIPPINES

IT IS NATURAL that, among an agrarian people, there should be many songs about rice and other food crops. This is another such Tagalog folk song, almost as popular among Filipinos in Hawaii as in their homeland. It is only one of many variations.

The melody shows the dominant influence of three hundred years of Spanish rule. The song uses the European diatonic major scale. The even-numbered four-bar ABAC pattern is also a Western form.

GLOSSARY: *Singkamas,* beans. *Talong,* egg plant *Sigarillas,* spinach. *Mani,* peanuts. *Sitao,* string beans. *Batao,* lima beans, *Patani,* turnips. *Nipa,* thatch made from the East Indian palm.

ANON.; ENG. AFTER AURELIA VIERNES ANONYMOUS

la-man do-on ay sa-ri-sa ri, Sing-ka-mas at ta-long, si-ga-rillas ma-ni, Si-tao, ba-tao pa-ta-ni.

gar-den is full, there is food for us all, Sing-ka-mas and ta-long, si-ga-rillas ma-ni, Si-tao, ba-tao, pa-ta-ni.

2 Kindol patola, upo't kalabasa.
At saka mayroon pang la banos, mustasa;
Sibuyas, kamates, baoang at luya,
Sa palibot ay puro linga.

All kinds of good things are found everywhere,
Of cabbage and squash there is plenty to spare,
Cucumbers and peas so tender and sweet,
And everything else good to eat.

Music of Asia 59

MENG-KU CHING KO
Mongolian Love Song
MONGOLIA

THIS LOVELY SONG is based upon a seven-tone scale that corresponds to the Dorian mode of the European church modal system. It is very unusual to find old Asian songs in seven-tone scales, even though such scales were propounded theoretically by ancient Chinese musical scholars. Most Asian music traditionally used the pentatonic scale as its foundation, with the added tones serving as embellishments to the principal tones. Such embellishments are impossible to show in Western notation and belong to the realm of the performer.

Charles Tien Wei Yun, from whom this version of the song was learned, gives the following advice: "Sing slowly and give yourself time to think of home—far away. If you just left home, sing it faster."

ANON.; ENG. AFTER C.T.W. YUN

ANON.; AS SUNG BY C.T.W. YUN

Moderately ♩ = 60

1. Tsai na yiao yuen di di___ fung, You wei how gu niang.
In my home-land___ far a-way, There's a fair young maid.

Zen men tsou kuo liaw ta di___tsang fung, Du yiao whi to pu twang di tsang
Past her tent you___ may go___walk-ing, There to find your glance by her beaut-y

whung. / stayed.

2. Ta na mei li di shia liang.
You will see her smiling face,

How shung hung ta yung.
Rosy sun-burned cheeks.

Ta na mei li ming mei di shiao yen,
Notice too her eyes are laughing,

How shung whan sung ming mei di yuh liang.
Like the new moon's bright and slender trace.

3. Wha yuen tso yi tsu shiao yang, Shui tsa ta sin pang,
Gentle lamb, I'd like to be, Lying by her side,

Za ta na tso na pi pien pu tuang, Ching ching da tsa wu aw sin sang.
Moon and stars overhead, While with her hand she gently caresses me.

KANG-TING SHING YUEH

New Moon Over Kangting

CHINA

long a-go, Knew great *liu-liu-dy* sor-row, But the *liu-liu-dy* with-er'd tree, Grows new *liu-liu-dy* blos-soms. New moon, new moon, crescent moon, Grows new *liu-liu-dy* blos-soms. 3. Hear the *liu-liu-dy* gong re-sound, Drums are *liu-liu-dy* beat-ing, Kang-ting *liu-liu-dy* sings a-loud, New life *liu-liu-dy* greet-ing.

New moon, new moon, crescent moon, New life *liu-liu-dy* greet-ing.

To the people of Asia the moon is not only an object of great beauty but also the symbol of many human qualities and situations—a heavenly sanctuary, the shape of a beautiful face, the epitome of gentleness and maternal love. The present song endows the new moon with the joys of seasonal rebirth and the realization of age-old hopes and aspirations for a better life. In the second verse a brief remembrance of past sorrows gives way to a vision of new blossoms from a withered tree.

The elements of syncopation in the accompaniment suggest the grace of movement characteristic of folk dancing of China.

The song originally came from Kangting, capital of Sikang. While the tune is old, the folk process accounts for the lyrics given here in English translation (unfortunately, the Chinese text was not available), which are of more recent origin.

The word *liuliudy* has no meaning.

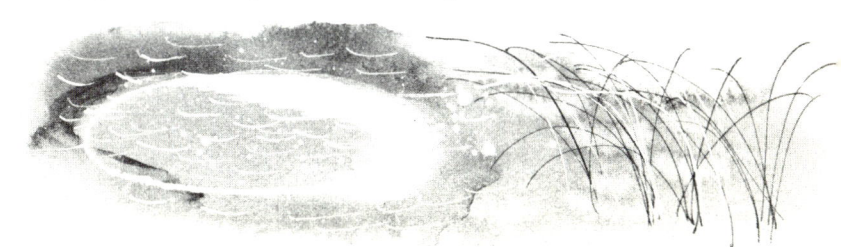

LAN HUA-HUA
Blue Flower
CHINA

This song comes from North Shensi, which has long been one of China's most depressed areas. In olden days its barren, mountainous, and sparsely populated land was used for growing the opium poppy and was an area often harassed by bandits.

Here the beautiful young girl Lan Hua-hua symbolizes youth who reject such customs of the past as the selling of daughters to meet heavy taxes (as sung in the third and fourth verses). The pledge of love in the last verse expresses defiance of the old custom of marriages arranged by parents for motives other than of true love.

Many twentieth-century Chinese folk songs and stories, such as this, have embodied concepts deriving from the Three Principles of the People—Nationalism, Democracy, and Livelihood—as formulated by Sun Yat-sen (father of the Chinese Republic, which replaced the Manchu dynasty in 1911). The sentiments of the lyrics of this song reflect that period, while the tune is probably of older origin. Sun Yat-sen, incidentally, spent six formative years of his life, until the age of nineteen, as a student at Iolani School in Honolulu.

The melody here is based on the pentatonic scale, characteristic of the Chinese folk song.

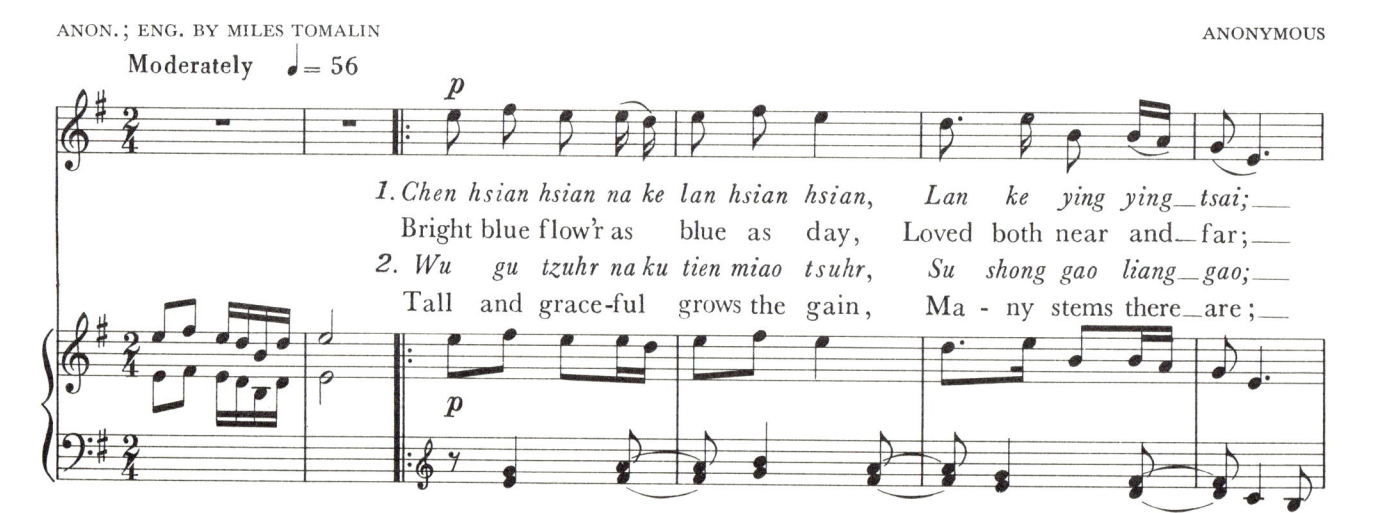

ANON.; ENG. BY MILES TOMALIN — ANONYMOUS

Moderately ♩ = 56

1. *Chen hsian hsian na ke lan hsian hsian, Lan ke ying ying tsai;*
   Bright blue flow'rs as blue as day, Loved both near and far;
2. *Wu gu tzuhr na ku tien miao tsuhr, Su shong gao liang gao;*
   Tall and graceful grows the gain, Many stems there are;

Sheng hsia i ke Lan Hua hua uhr, Shih shih ai shih jen.
None so bright and none so gay, As our pretty Lan Hua-hua.
I shuh sang shung ti nuer, Su sang Lan Hua-hua hao.
Of the maids who live on the plain, None so fair as Lan Hua-hua.

3. *Tsung yueh li na guh so mei, Er yueh li ting;*
Brief the time and harsh the law, Hard the bargain driven;
4. *Lan Hua-hua na guh shia jiaw leh Dung tsang shi yu tsao;*
Old is he and on his face Many an evil scar;

San yueh li chiao ta chien Suh yueh li ying.
One fine day is Lan Hua-hua To the highest bidder given.
Tsao chien tsou chia di hou lau tsuh, Hao chien i tso fen.
Living death is in this place, Stay no longer Lan Hua-hua.

5. So— ti sang na— guh,
I come knock-ing at your door,
Yang zou wheh tri gao;— Wuo mao sang— guh shing ming,— Wong— ni cha li pao.—
Rise and let me through;— It is I, poor Lan Hua-hua,— None I dare to trust but you.—

6. Bu ai ni na guh tung— lai,
You are gen-tle,— you are kind,
Bu ai— ni si; Tang— ai— guh guh ti,— Er— suh— i.
Young and brave you are;— I give you my heart and mind,— Take the love of Lan Hua-hua.

DORAJI TAHRYUNG
Song of Bluebells
KOREA

One of the best-known songs of Korea, this tells of a girl dreaming of love. There are many local versions. The song often accompanies a lovely free-flowing dance in which young girls, wearing the traditional gaily colored costumes for the young and unmarried, move among the mountain flowers gathering the edible roots of the bluebell plant.

Although the history of song literature of the world shows that a good deal of borrowing takes place, it is probably only a coincidence that the first few bars of this melody, like those of "Hills of Arirang" and many other songs of Asia, outline the major triad of Western tonality.

The triple time of many Korean songs distinguishes them from neighboring Japanese, Chinese, and Ryukyuan music, which is usually in duple time.

ANON.; ENG. AFTER KEUM NYU PARK   ANONYMOUS

Music of Asia 69

Do - ra - ji, do - ra - ji, do - ra - ji,
Blue - bells, blue - bells, love - ly blue - bells,

Sim - sim san - chun - eh pek - do - ra ji.
Deep in the moun - tains my blue - bells grow.

Hahn du bu - ri - mahn keh - yuh - doh Teh kwang - chu - ri
Gath - er - ing blue - bells in dark val - leys, Bas - kets are

su-ri-sal - sal da-nuh-nun-dah. Eh heh___ ya, eh heh___ ya,
near-ly full__ with__ just one or two. Ta da di dum, ta da di dum,

eh heh_____ ya,_____ Eh heh ra nan-dah ji-wha-cha_____
ta da di da_____ dum, Tum ta di da di dum, Love - ly

jo - tah. Neh-ka neh-kan chang-ul, su-ri-sal-sal____ tah-noh-kin-da.
blue - bells. O my darl - ing,____ do you know_ how____ I long for you?

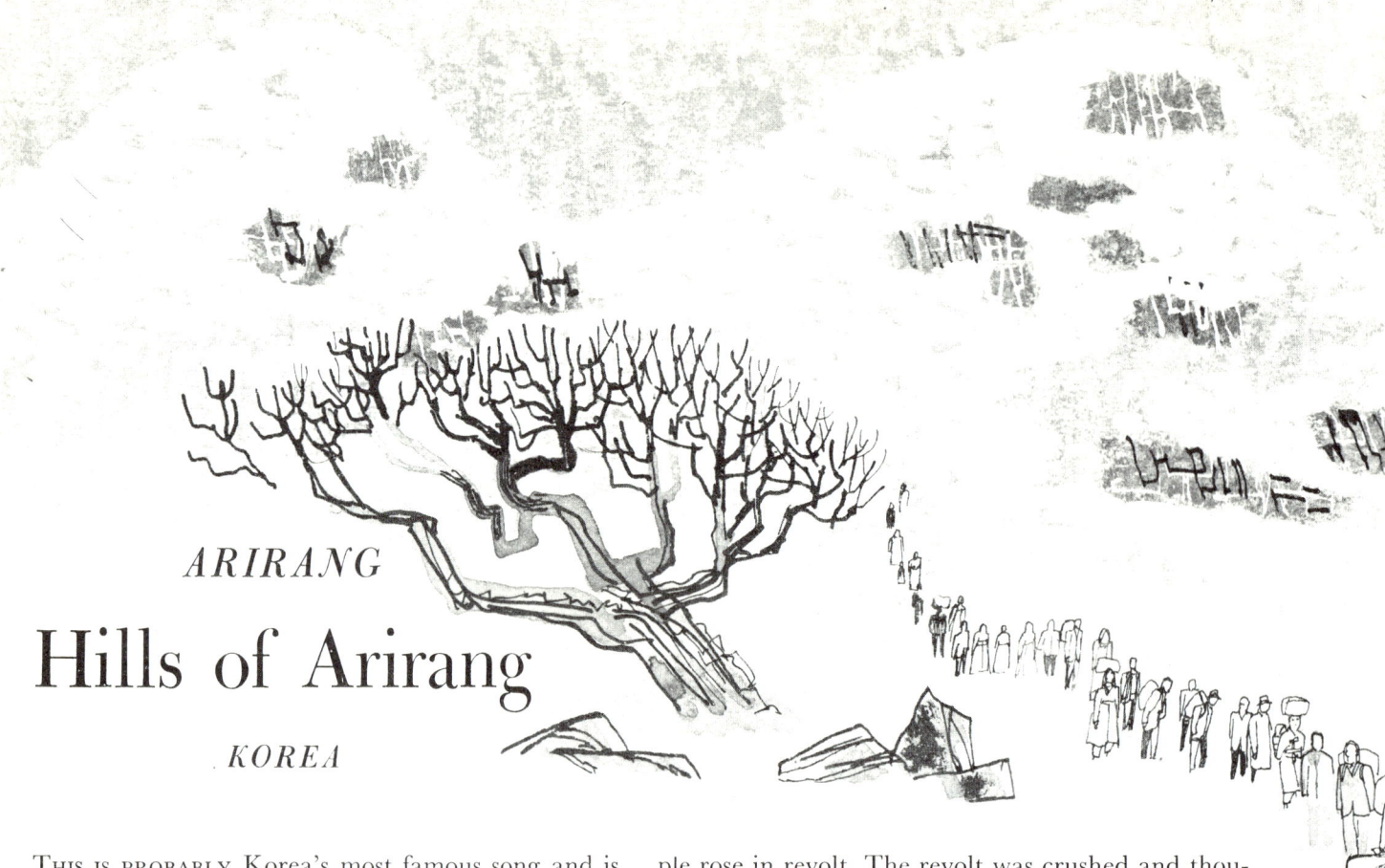

ARIRANG
Hills of Arirang
KOREA

This is probably Korea's most famous song and is very well known in Hawaii and by people of other lands who have visited Korea. It is said to be at least two thousand years old. As with most old folk songs there are countless versions with subjects varying from tender love messages to sentiments of national pride and patriotism.

Under the duress of foreign occupation and with a long history of invasions from countries of the Asiatic mainland and from Japan, the Korean people have invested much of their song, drama, literature, and art with qualities of strength and determination to surmount life's problems, resist the invaders, and survive for a better future.

One explanation of the song's origin is that there was once a despotic emperor against whom the people rose in revolt. The revolt was crushed and thousands of patriots were led across the hills of Arirang to be executed. This is said to have been the song the patriots sang on their way to execution. The words "Crossing the hills of Arirang" have now come to mean that one must surmount life's many vicissitudes and meet squarely the challenge to happiness.

The song is usually sung with a combination of tenderness and strength. As mentioned on page 8, it is impossible to notate all the in-between tones of the music of Asia. In the score given here only the principle notes of the melody are noted. Each performer usually creates his own interpretation, adding notes and inflections here and there according to his own feelings. The second verse given here is a love-song version.

ANON.; ENG. AFTER KEUM NYU PARK   ANONYMOUS

Moderately slow ♩ = 96

A - ri-rang, A - ri-rang, A - ra - ri -
A - ri-rang, A - ri-rang, A - ra - ri -

72 *Folk Songs Hawaii Sings*

2 *Arirang, Arirang, Arariyo,*
Arirang kogero nuhmuhkanda.
Naruhl parigo kanunimun,
Shimyido motgasuh palpyungnanda.

Arirang, Arirang, Arariyo,
Crossing the hills of Arirang.
If you leave me, sweetheart,
You will be footsore within a mile.

Music of Asia

KEH-GI-NA-CHING-CHING-NAH-NEH
A New Spring Is Coming
KOREA

KOREA IS A LAND of rolling hills and fertile valleys extending from Mt. Pektu near the Yalu River in the north to Cheju Island near the southern tip. The national flower is the *mugung* (Hibiscus rose-sinensis), known as the Rose of Korea. Its purple and white blossoms closely resemble the hibiscus, to which family it belongs.

This very old Korean folk song, which exists in many versions, sings of the coming of spring, when the *mugung* will bloom. During the long Japanese occupation, the Korean people imbued this song with the meaning that one day soon the spring of freedom and independence would blossom again in the land. For this reason the Japanese military authorities banned this song and likewise "Arirang," which had a similar connotation.

The refrain, which gives the song its Korean title, is a poetic expression of happiness and exhilaration. A literal translation of the verse goes: "From Mt. Pektu (White-head) for three thousand *li*, in the valleys of the *mugung,* a new spring is coming." The song is so short that it has been arranged here with English verses following the Korean.

ANON.; ENG. AFTER HALLA HUHM   ANONYMOUS

Fast ♩.=132

Keh-gi-na-ching-ching-nah-neh,____ Pek-tu-sun hul-law-saw pan-doh sam-chul-li

74   *Folk Songs Hawaii Sings*

Mu-gung wha tong-san-eh seh-pum-i wat-neh. Keh-gi-na-ching-ching nah-neh,— From Pek-tu moun-tain for three thou-sand *li* — the flow-ers are bloom-ing, a new spring is com-ing! Keh-gi-na-ching-ching-nah-neh!

KUNBAM TAHRYUNG
Song of Roasted Chestnuts
KOREA

A VENDOR STROLLS along a snowy village street with his young assistant and hawks his tasty ware. How delicious hot roasted or steamed chestnuts are on a cold winter day!

This song may be sung as a solo or as a simple question-and-answer song with chorus. The first voice part may be taken by the whole chorus or by one singer, and the second by another singer. If a chorus is used, the second voice part is better with two or three singers.

ANON.; ENG. AFTER KEUM NYU PARK ANONYMOUS

Briskly ♩ = 100

1st Voice: Nun-yi ohn-da, Oh ya! Nun-yi wa-yo, uh-deh-suh, kyung-sah-nan-yi ha-nul-yi?

White snow is fall-ing. Fall-ing! White snow is fall-ing. Fall-ing! Tell me, from where does the snow come?

76 Folk Songs Hawaii Sings

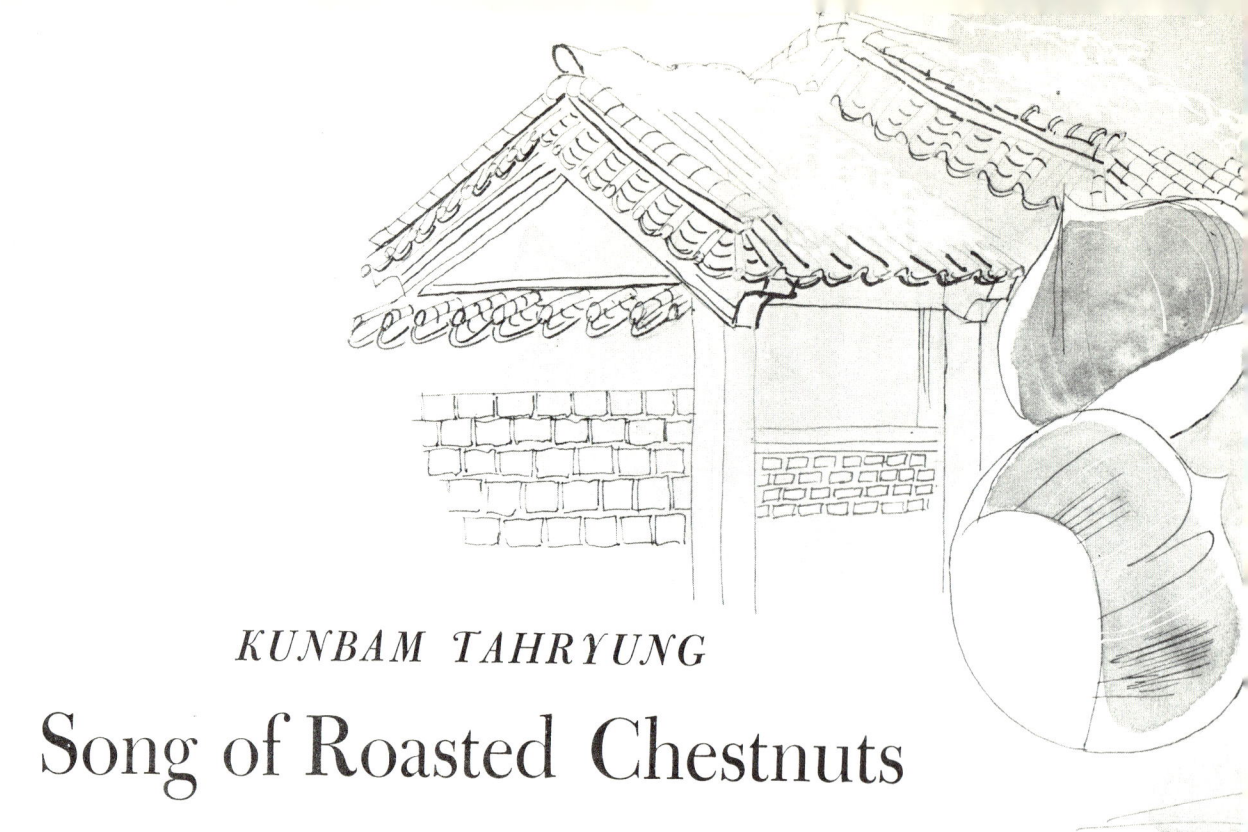

1st Voice / *Both*

Uh - ra - ul - sa hin - nun - yi - ohn - dan ul - sa - jot - neh.___ I - bam - eh
Win - ter skies___ are bu - sy as e - ver and that's where it comes from!___ Hot roast - ed

2nd Voice (Shout)

kun - bam - i - yo ___ oh - yeh, Sal - mun bam - i - yo - kun - ah. Cho ta!
tast - y chest - nuts, ___ Buy a hot one, steamed ones too! Oh yum - yum!

Music of Asia 77

TUHL TAHRYUNG

Weaving Song

KOREA

ANONYMOUS   ANONYMOUS

Moderately with gentle swing ♩.= 72

1. Kai - ka chit - ne, Kai - ka chit - ne,
2. Ta - ki u - ne, Ta - ki u - ne,
3. Heh - ga du - ne, Heh - ga du - ne,

78 *Folk Songs Hawaii Sings*

THIS IS A WEAVER'S SONG, and it is said that the texture of the emotional life of a weaver may be expressed in that of the material he weaves. A tight weft with many concentrated threads may represent intense unhappiness. A loose weft may mean he is happy with other things as well as with his weaving, as found in the quiet movement of this song. The verses suggest that the weaver's work begins in the evening and continues to sunrise as can be seen in a a literal translation of the lyrics by Halla Huhm: "Dogs are barking, dogs are barking, o'er yonder village barking—oh, yes!" In the second verse change to "cock is crowing," and in the third, to "sun is rising." The refrain is made up of words that have no particular meaning.

Pronunciation Guide

THIS IS NOT INTENDED as a complete guide but it may help to avoid the worst mistakes. Whenever possible, try and hear the words as spoken by a native speaker of the language, and keep in mind that every language has its regional differences.

As used in this volume, vowels have the following approximate values:

a	like the *a* in *father*
e	like the *a* in *bay*
eh	like the *e* in *met*
i	like the *e* in *meet*
o	like the *oa* in *boat*
ow	like the *ow* in *how*
u	like the *oo* in *too*
uh	like the *u* in *but*

In general avoid making diphthongs out of pure vowels, e.g., pronounce *a* as in *father*, not as the *au* sound in *found*.

The hamzuh or inverted apostrophe is used in Hawaiian and to indicate the glottal attack on vowels and represents dropped consonants. It is usually used between repeated vowels as in the word *o'o* (ripe, poke), which sounds like the English *oh-oh!* To omit the glottal attack or to put it in the wrong place often changes the meaning of the word.

Hamzuhs are omitted from proper names and place names. However, proper names and place names used in this book should be pronounced as follows:

Hapu'u	Kina'u	Niuli'i
Hawai'i	Kipu'upu'u	Nu'uanu
Hi'iaka	Lana'i	O'ahu
Kaho'olawe	Laua'e	Puku'i
Kaka'ako	Li'a	Pu'u Kalani
Kamaka'eha	Lili'uokalani	Wai'ale'ale
Kaua'i	Moloka'i	
Kauna'oa	Ni'ihau	

Consonants are pronounced approximately as in English, with the following exceptions:

Hawaiian: *w* is pronounced as *v* after *i* and *e;* as *w* after *u* and *o;* and as *v* or *w* after *a* or when used initially.

Japanese: *n* is a separate syllable and is often prolonged on a note all of its own; *f* is a combination of English *f* and *h* but more aspirate; *g* is often softened to *ng*.

Korean and Chinese: Explosive consonants *t* and *d*, *p* and *b*, *k* and *g*, sound more alike than in English, i.e., the *t* is gentle and sounds more like *d*, etc.

Samoan: *g* becomes *ng*, thus *mauga* (mountain) is pronounced *maunga*.

Filipino: *ng* is pronounced as *nung* with a very short *u* when it occurs as a word by itself.

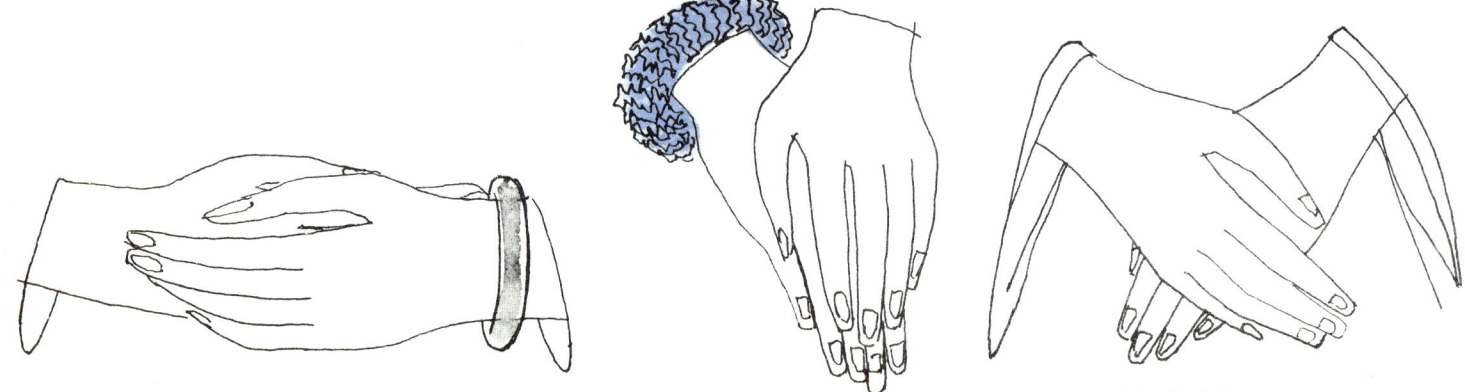

The manual attitudes of the Chinese, Hawaiian, and Japanese in taking their final bow

Selected Bibliography

THE FOLLOWING is a short selected list of currently available collections containing folk songs suitable or easily adaptable to school use. It is provided through the courtesy of Barbara B. Smith, Associate Professor of Music, University of Hawaii.

CHINESE
   Liu, Liang-mo and Modoi, Evelyn: *China Sings.* Fisher, New York, 1945.

FILIPINO
   Magdamo, Priscilla V.: *Folk Songs of the Visayas* (Vol. 1). Silliman Univ. Foundation, Dumaguete City, 1957
   Reysio-Cruz, Emilia: *Filipino Folk Songs.* Community Publishers, Manila, 1950

   Tapales, Ramon: *Singing and Growing* (Philippine Edition). Bookman, Manila, c. 1952

JAPANESE
   Cooperative Recreation Service, Inc.: *A Sampler of Japanese Songs.* Informal Music Service, Delaware, Ohio, 1958
   Hattori, Ryutaro: *Japanese Folk Songs* (3rd ed.). Japan Times, Tokyo, 1957

KOREAN
   Lee, Kang Nyum: *Korean Folk-Songs.* National Music Research Society of Korea, Seoul, 1954
   Korean Research and Information Office: *Korea, Land of Song.* Washington, D.C., n.d.